Preface

This report was commissioned by the trustees of the British Medical Foundation for AIDS in April 1988 and completed by Paul Sieghart immediately before his death on 12 December 1988. Paul Sieghart was a brilliant and distinguished writer and law reformer, who devoted much of his life to the pursuit of justice and human rights in Britain and abroad. Having himself left Austria as a child to escape the Anschluss, he understood only too well the need for vigilance against threats to people's fundamental rights and dignities. Both he and the trustees came to see the advent of AIDS as such a threat, raising questions of discrimination, intrusion into individual privacy, and coercive powers of the State.

Following his resignation from the commercial bar in 1966, Paul Sieghart held several appointments of distinction. He was Chairman of the Executive Committee of Justice, the British Section of the International Commission of Jurists, for ten years until October 1988. On the night of his death he learned that he had been nominated by Justice for the Human Rights Prize of the Council of Europe. He was founder and first Vice-Chairman of the Council for Science and Society, reflecting his continuing interest in the social and ethical implications of scientific advances, and Chairman of the European Human Rights Foundation. He served on the Catholic Bishops' Commission for International Justice and Peace and Working Party on Human Rights. He was honoured with a personal chair in law at King's College, in the University of London.

Paul Sieghart worked tirelessly until his death, completing both this report and a companion version which examines the same issues from a broader international perspective, rather than focussing on the United Kingdom, together with several other ventures. His previous publications include books on human rights law, privacy of computer data, a computer programme for teaching medical ethics, and numerous articles. He was an experienced and effective communicator, noted for his chairing of televised debates and discussions.

The BMA Foundation for AIDS is honoured to publish Paul Sieghart's work, and trusts that it will be widely read and its message taken to heart.

Dr John Marks
Chairman of Trustees

A|DS
& HUMAN RIGHTS

A UK PERSPECTIVE

Paul Sieghart

Chairman, European Human Rights Foundation;
Founder and first Vice-Chairman, Council for Science
and Society, London; Honorary Visiting Professor of Law,
King's College, University of London.

The author is greatly indebted to Susan Hulton and
Dr Michael Thomas for their valuable assistance in the
preparation of this paper, and to Dr Roy Porter
of the Wellcome Institute for the History of Medicine,
and the Panos Institute, for the provision of some
useful references.

British Medical Association
Foundation for AIDS
1989

AIDS and Human Rights
by Paul Sieghart

A publication from the British Medical Association
Foundation for AIDS

Director	Dr John Dawson
Administrator	Hilary Curtis
Administrative assistant	Lynne Evans
Designer	Glynn Bennallick

British Library Cataloguing in Publication Data:
*British Medical Association Foundation for AIDS
Sieghart, Paul*

AIDS AND HUMAN RIGHTS.-UK ed.

ISBN 1 871973 01 5 (paper cover)
      1 871973 00 7 (hard cover)

Published by:
British Medical Association Foundation for AIDS
BMA House
Tavistock Square
London
WC1H 9JP

Printed by:
Chameleon Press Limited
5-25 Burr Road
London
SW18 4SG

Contents

5 Conclusions

6 Notes

Table of Authorities

Index

Introduction

We emphasise the need in AIDS prevention programmes to protect human rights and human dignity. Discrimination against, and stigmatisation of, HIV-infected people and people with AIDS and population groups undermine public health and must be avoided.

– World Summit of Ministers of Health, London Declaration on AIDS Prevention, 28 January 1988.

The Forty-first World Health Assembly, Strongly convinced that respect for human rights and dignity of HIV-infected people and people with AIDS, and of members of population groups, is vital to the success of national AIDS prevention and control programmes and of the global strategy URGES Member States, particularly in devising and carrying out national programmes for the prevention and control of HIV infection and AIDS to protect the human rights and dignity of HIV-infected people and people with AIDS, and of members of population groups, and to avoid discriminatory action against and stigmatisation of them in the provision of services, employment and travel [and] to ensure the confidentiality of HIV testing

– Resolution WHA41.24, adopted in Geneva on 13 May 1988.

The purpose of this paper is to consider the legitimacy, in terms of the international law of human rights, of public health policies which governments might wish to adopt in order to limit the spread of AIDS within their populations.

AIDS is essentially a matter falling within the specialised expertise of medical science and public health; human rights are essentially a subject within the specialised domain of national and international law.In order to discuss the relationship between these two things, it is therefore as well to begin by explaining some of their leading features, and outlining their boundaries.

1 AIDS

1.1 The acronym AIDS stands for 'acquired immune deficiency syndrome' – that is, a cluster of symptoms manifested by patients whose immunological defences have been severely compromised, and who have therefore fallen prey to a variety of infectious or other illnesses. When a patient manifests this syndrome, there is a very high probability that he or she will die from such an AIDS-related illness, usually within a year or two. At present, there is no vaccine or cure for AIDS, and no treatment which does more than delay its progression.

1.2 AIDS is exhibited only by patients who have been infected by an organism belonging to a group now known as human immunodeficiency viruses (HIV). Normally, when the human body encounters a virus, its immune system is activated and the infective organism is eventually eliminated, so that the patient recovers and can no longer infect others. However, HIV attacks parts of that immune system, with the result that:

- the patient is left with no defence against 'opportunistic' infections, which might pass quite unnoticed in an uninfected individual, but may now prove fatal;

- the patient may die from a cancer which he or she would otherwise not have developed;

- the patient is unable to eliminate the virus itself, so that once infected he or she remains infectious for life.

1.3   A person who becomes infected with HIV becomes potentially infectious to others shortly afterwards and within about two weeks at most. At this stage, a sufficiently sophisticated test can detect the virus in the patient's blood. At some time later – which may be as long as six months – he or she will begin to develop antibodies to the virus by an immunological reaction. When a detectable concentration of antibodies is reached, 'sero-conversion' is said to have occurred. These antibodies too can be established by a variety of blood tests, some of which are more reliable than others. If and when antibodies are present in sufficient concentration, these tests will generally show that the patient is 'HIV positive'.

1.4   Depending on the sensitivity and selectivity of the particular test used, HIV tests may sometimes produce a 'false positive' result – that is, appear to show that a patient is HIV positive when he or she has not in fact been infected by the virus; or they may produce a 'false negative' result – that is, appear to show that a patient is HIV negative when he or she has in fact been infected by the virus, and has already started to develop antibodies. The earliest tests produced a high proportion of false positives, and also some false negatives, because they could not detect the early production of antibodies. The best tests currently in use give accurate results in over 99% of cases.

1.5   The disease has only been identified and studied for about 7 years. So far, the proportion of patients who have developed the full syndrome after having been initially infected has been of the order of 35%-50%. The period between these two events – during which the patient will generally have no symptoms, and may therefore well not even know that he or she is harbouring the infection – has sometimes been as little as a few months, but is usually much longer. The average is thought at present to be about 7 to 8 years; however, as more experience is gained with more patients over a longer time, both the maximum period and the proportion who eventually develop the full syndrome can be expected to rise. Also, there is already more than one type of HIV, producing different reactions over different time-scales. It is therefore not impossible that, over time, all HIV-positive patients will eventually develop AIDS.

1.6   In any given population at present, therefore, for every patient manifesting the full AIDS syndrome there will be a far larger number of persons who are infected with HIV but are not (or not yet) showing any symptoms. How many that will be will vary from one population to another: in some cases, it could be as many as 100.

1.7 Alongside the classical AIDS syndrome, some patients will develop HIV neuro-psychiatric disease, initially characterised by loss of short-term memory and ability to concentrate, and eventually progressing to blindness, incontinence, and dementia.

1.8 The principal vehicles of infection are:

- the blood of an infected person;
- the semen or the vaginal and cervical secretions of an infected person.

1.9 In order to acquire the infection, the contaminated fluid (blood, semen, or vaginal and cervical secretions) must enter the bloodstream of the recipient. This is possible through:

- direct entry to the bloodstream, e.g. through a syringe or other skin-piercing device, or through a needlestick injury, or in the course of surgery, or through an open cut or an abrasion, or through the placenta before birth;
- a permeable mucous membrane, such as those of the glans penis, the vulva or vagina, the rectum, or the mouth.

1.10 For practical purposes, this means that the infection can only be transmitted from one human being to another:

- in the course of sexual activities involving the genitalia of one of them and either the genitalia or some other mucosa of the other;
- parenterally, that is through hypodermic punctures, or in the course of surgery, or through other blood-to-blood contacts such as transfusions;
- perinatally, that is by a mother to her baby before, during, or shortly after birth.

1.11 In the developed countries, AIDS was first recognised as a result of HIV infection predominantly acquired through:

- anal sexual intercourse between homosexual men;
- the sharing of contaminated needles by intravenous drug abusers;
- contaminated blood products given to people with haemophilia;
- contaminated blood transfusions.

1.12 Increasingly and in all regions of the world, the infection is also transmitted through heterosexual intercourse.

1.13 On present knowledge, it appears to be impossible to acquire the infection through:

- insect or other parasite vectors;
- droplet infection (e.g. sneezing or coughing);
- saliva, whether by kissing, drinking or eating from the same utensils, or otherwise;
- contact with a common external object (e.g. cutlery, crockery, towels or other linens, or a lavatory seat);
- water (e.g. common use of a washbasin or a swimming pool);
- other forms of social contact (e.g. hand-shaking, non-sexual embraces, sports, etc.);
- being a blood donor.

1.14 Following the practice of the World Health Organisation,[1] the expression AIDS will often be used in the rest of this paper to include not only the full clinical syndrome, but the entire spectrum of health problems associated with HIV infection.

2 *Human Rights*

2.0.1 For centuries, philosophers, moralists, politicians and others have debated about the nature of rights; whether rights can be classified into different categories; whether there are some rights which are universal in the sense that they are 'inherent' in, and 'inalienable' by, everyone; if so, from what antecedents such rights can be derived; and what is the relationship between rights and laws.

2.0.2 These debates continue. Meanwhile, however, the international community of nations has since 1945 established a binding code of international human rights *law*.[2] This is laid down in a series of instruments which include:

- the UN Charter of 1945;

- the Universal Declaration of Human Rights, adopted in 1948;

- the twin International Covenants, which entered into force in 1976: one on Civil and Political Rights and the other on Economic, Social and Cultural Rights;

- regional treaties like the European Convention on Human Rights (in force since 1953), the European Social Charter (1965), the American Convention on Human Rights (1978), and the African Charter of Human Rights and Peoples' Rights (1986);

- some 20 or more other treaties, both global and regional, which cover some specific rights in greater detail.

2.0.3 This code declares and protects around 40 or 50 different rights, each specifically defined, for 'everyone ... without distinction of any kind, such as race, colour, sex, language, religion, political or other opinion, national or social origin, property, birth or other status'. Among these rights are:

- a right to life;

- a right to health;

- a right to liberty and security of person;

- freedom from inhuman or degrading treatment or punishment;

- a right to freedom of movement;

- a right to privacy;

- a right to marry and found a family;

- a right to work;

- a right to education;

- a right to social security, assistance and welfare.

2.0.4 For every right, there must be a corresponding duty, imposed on someone other than the holder of the right. To the right of a tenant to occupy some premises, for instance, there corresponds a duty on the landlord and on all others not to trespass there against the tenant's wishes. In the case of human rights, the corresponding duty falls on the State, which is obliged to have in place such laws and administrative arrangements as will ensure, to the best of its abilities, that the human rights of its inhabitants will be respected. So, for example, to the human right to life there corresponds a duty of the State not itself to take the life of its citizens, and to have appropriate laws, police forces, courts and prisons which will, so far as reasonably possible, deter the commission of murder or manslaughter.

2.0.5 No one today disputes the fact that this code exists, and that it is *legally* binding on the member States i.e. the international community of nations who have adhered to it. Few nations yet conform to it in every detail, and some still violate it to a greater or lesser degree. But every such violation today is not merely to be lamented or condemned on grounds of morality or humanity: it constitutes a breach of binding international *law*.

2.0.6 At the international level, the legal *enforcement* of this code still leaves much to be desired. There is not yet any single international court with universal compulsory jurisdiction over the world's sovereign states, let alone an international force of police or bailiffs to enforce the judgments of such a court. However, at the *regional* level there are now some quite effective means of enforcement. For example, the decisions of the supranational organs at Strasbourg (the European Commission and the European Court of Human Rights), which were established by the European Convention on Human Rights, are in practice universally obeyed by the 21 Member States of the Council of Europe which are parties to this Convention. Likewise, more than half of all the world's sovereign States are now bound by the two International Covenants on Human Rights, and so accept the jurisdiction of the supervisory organs which they establish.[3] In addition, an increasing number of these States allow individual complaints against them to be directed to one of these organs, the Human Rights Committee established by the International Covenant on Civil and Political Rights.

2.1 Human rights and civil rights

2.1.1 In order to be effective, human rights must be protected by law, and the law must provide a remedy for any established violations of them. While it is valuable to have supervision by international organs, the most important place for such laws to be in force, and for such remedies to be available, is on the national (often called the 'domestic' or 'municipal') plane.

2.1.2 Two schools of thought exist about the relationship between international law and national law. The 'monist' school holds that there is only one system of law, of which international and national law are no more than two aspects. Where this view prevails – as in the USA and in many European countries – the national courts will apply international law directly, provided that its provisions are sufficiently clear and precise for that purpose. In those countries, such provisions are called 'self-executing', and some parts of international human rights law may therefore be directly applicable, over and above any national 'civil rights' law.

2.1.3 The 'dualist' school, on the other hand, maintains that national and international law are distinct and separate, and that national courts can only apply the provisions of international law if the domestic legislature has expressly 'incorporated' them into the national law. A number of such countries have in fact carried out such an incorporation for one or another of the international human rights treaties by which they have chosen to become bound.

2.1.4 A good example of a legal system that is still almost entirely dualist is that of the United Kingdom – that is, the courts of the UK cannot directly apply any provisions of an international treaty unless the UK Parliament has enacted specific legislation which incorporates it. No part of the code of international human rights law has in fact yet been so incorporated; accordingly, anyone in the UK who wishes to complain of an alleged infringement of any of his or her human rights protected by that code cannot bring that complaint, formulated in that fashion, before the UK courts, but will have to follow the circuitous route of taking his or her case to the European supervisory organs in Strasbourg; if a favourable judgment is obtained there, the UK government will then abide by it.

2.1.5 However, this does not mean that human rights lack all protection in UK national law, for the UK has for several centuries protected what it calls 'civil rights' and 'civil liberties' by domestic laws which form the analogues – and indeed the historical predecessors – of the 'human' rights which are now declared in the international code. In practice, therefore, virtually all the human rights declared in that code are protected on the domestic plane by UK national law – but as 'civil rights' and 'civil liberties' rather than as 'human rights'.

2.1.6 Similarly, the USA has not yet adhered to any of the international human rights treaties (apart from the UN Charter), but the Bill of Rights incorporated in its written Constitution protects many of the same rights on the domestic plane – as do the constitutions of many Commonwealth countries.

2.1.7 Henceforth, whenever a 'human right' is mentioned in this paper, it is to be taken as a reference to a right specifically declared by some part of the international code – that is, as a legal right established in *international law*, and not merely a right which one might wish, on religious, moral, or humanitarian grounds, that people should have. Such a right will often already constitute a 'civil right' or 'civil liberty' under the domestic law of the country concerned – most commonly in its written Constitution, if it has one – and be protected accordingly.

2.1.8 If it is not already so protected, then any violation of it by the State concerned may not constitute a breach of its own domestic law, but will still constitute a breach of its obligations under international human rights law. The conduct of such a State will therefore be no less illegal, though it may prove more difficult to obtain a *legal* remedy for it. However, the forum of international public opinion provides a remedy which is becoming increasingly effective: few governments are willing to be branded as international law-breakers, especially in the matter of how they treat their inhabitants.

2.2 Conflicts of interest

2.2.1 Most of the problems in the field of human rights are presented where there is a conflict between the claims of an individual human being to pursue his or her own interest, and the claims of other members of the same society to restrict that pursuit because it would, or might, harm *their* interests. It is one of the principal functions of the international code of human rights law to seek to resolve such conflicts.

2.2.2 The means by which the code does this are to define many of the rights with which it deals by reference to their boundaries. For example, it defines a general 'right to life', and then immediately proceeds to set out the circumstances in which life may nonetheless be legitimately taken – e.g. in execution of a death sentence passed by a court fulfilling all the code's requirements of competence, independence, and impartiality, and all the required safeguards in the proceedings; or in self-defence; and so on.

2.2.3   Some of the rights which the code declares – such as freedom from slavery, and from torture or 'inhuman or degrading treatment or punishment' – are absolute, and may not be limited or restricted in any circumstances, even in time of war or public emergency threatening the life of the nation. However, in the case of several of the other rights which it declares, the code uses a standard formula, couched in the language of limitations and restrictions, in order to define their boundaries, and an understanding of the form and effect of this is essential for what follows in this paper.

2.2.4   First, in all such cases the code declares a 'core' right – e.g. 'everyone has the right to respect for his private and family life, his home and his correspondence'.[4] The code then proceeds to say that there shall be no interference with this core right (or that it shall not be restricted or limited) save only as may be 'provided (or prescribed) by law' and is 'necessary in a democratic society' for the protection of one or more of a list of (public) interests. This list generally includes such things as national security, the prevention of crime, and the rights and freedoms of others. Most important for the purposes of this paper, it almost always includes 'public health'.

2.2.5   It is crucially important to understand the effect of such a provision. It does *not*, as an uninformed first reader of the texts might be forgiven for imagining, take away with one hand what has just been given with the other. The universally established case-law (often called the 'constant jurisprudence') of the international organs which are called upon to interpret and apply the code has been unanimous in holding that any State wishing to justify any interference with, or limitation or restriction of, any declared 'core' right has the burden of proving affirmatively that the restriction was:

- 'prescribed by law', and
- 'necessary'
- in a democratic society
- for the protection of one or other of the listed interests.

Even then, the restriction will not be found justifiable if it strikes at the very heart of the right concerned.

2.2.6 This 'constant jurisprudence' is being developed among all the international organs which are authorised to interpret different parts of the code. However, since it was established more than 20 years before any of the others, by far the largest contribution to it so far has been that of the European Court of Human Rights in relation to the European Convention, by which all the 21 Member States of the Council of Europe are bound. Inevitably, therefore, the bulk of the references to decided cases in the rest of this paper will be to cases decided by this Court; one must, however, bear in mind that the language of all the international instruments is very similar, so that the other international tribunals are very likely to come to similar conlusions.

2.2.7 The following summary of the general principles which the European Court of Human Rights has enunciated will serve better than anything to explain the relationship between the 'core' rights declared by the code, and the boundaries for those rights delineated by the 'restriction' or 'limitation' clauses which it contains:

2.2.7.1 The adjective 'necessary' is synonymous neither with 'indispensable' nor with the loose test of 'reasonable' or 'desirable'. What the test of necessity connotes is a requirement that the State must establish a 'pressing social need' for the interference.[5]

2.2.7.2 The initial responsibility for securing the rights and freedoms enshrined in the provisions of the Convention lies with the contracting States. Accordingly, the Convention gives those States a 'margin of appreciation' – that is, a discretion to use their special knowledge of conditions within their countries to decide how best to implement the provisions of the Convention.[6]

2.2.7.3 Nevertheless, States do not have an unlimited margin of appreciation. The domestic margin of appreciation goes hand in hand with an international supervision.[7]

2.2.7.4 The supervision by the Commission and the Court is not limited to ascertaining whether a respondent State exercised its discretion reasonably, carefully and in good faith. Even if it did, its conduct may not necessarily be in compliance with the criteria of the Convention.[8]

2.2.7.5   The hallmarks of 'a democratic society' are pluralism, tolerance, and broadmindedness.[9]

2.2.7.6   The test to be satisfied by the respondent State (and the burden is on it) is whether the interference complained of corresponded to a pressing social need, whether it was 'proportionate' to a legitimate aim pursued to meet that need, and whether the reasons given by the national authorities to justify it are relevant and sufficient under the relevant Article of the Convention.[10]

2.2.7.7   The criterion of necessity requires consideration of the nature of the aim pursued.[11]

2.2.7.8   It is also relevant to consider whether informed opinion in the respondent State has suggested that the impugned interference with the right concerned could be removed without serious adverse consequences.[12]

2.2.7.9   Another factor which should be considered is the breadth of the restriction on the right concerned. The greater the breadth, the closer the scrutiny called for.[13]

2.2.7.10   The fourth relevant factor in applying the test of necessity is the public interest involved in the free exercise of the right concerned in the particular circumstances of the case. It is not enough to consider only the adverse effect on the individuals on whom the restriction is to be imposed: one also has to consider the effect on society in general of imposing restrictions of this kind on some of its members. The greater the public interest in the unfettered exercise of the relevant right, the more difficult will it be for the State to justify the restrictions it has imposed.[14] Indeed, where the public has 'a vital interest' in the exercise of the right, the State needs to show that it is 'absolutely certain' that its unrestricted exercise would have the adverse consequences alleged by the State.[15]

2.2.7.11   Although a fifth relevant factor is the practice of other State Parties to the Convention, this does not mean that absolute uniformity is required.[16] If a respondent State's practice is unusually restrictive in comparison with the practice of the other State Parties to the Convention, this will obviously increase the prospects of persuading the Commission or the Court to hold that there is a breach. If the incapacities with regard to the right concerned are sanctions and preventive measures of an unusual kind, the question of their justification as measures necessary in a democratic society has to be considered with special care.[17]

3 *AIDS and Human Rights*

3.0   Following these explanations, we can begin to consider the problems which the current and prospective spread of AIDS infection are likely to present in the context of human rights, and what options there may be for resolving them.

3.1 Lessons from history

3.1.1   Within recorded history, there has been no shortage of epidemics. Apart from recurrent outbreaks of cholera, typhoid, influenza, poliomyelitis, etc., perhaps the most dramatic have been the pandemics of bubonic plague in Europe between the 14th and 18th centuries. On those occasions, the mortality was sometimes such as to reduce whole populations to a fraction of their former size – despite the panic measures taken to prevent or limit the spread of the disease.

3.1.2   Among those measures – at all events before the mechanisms of infection became more fully understood – one of the most important was to try to identify, and then eliminate, the first cause of the disease. Unfortunately, this only too frequently became a search for a human scapegoat. During the Black Death of the 14th century, for instance, Jews were the prime suspects, and were massacred all over Europe. A little later, epidemics were blamed on the commission of sin, and the mob's venom was turned on suspected sinners. In similar vein, there were hunts for witches, or for members of other unpopular groups suspected of having poisoned the wells.

3.1.3   Nor was this simply a phenomenon of the superstitious Middle Ages: as late as the first half of the enlightened 19th century in Europe, medical practitioners were suspected of having caused outbreaks of cholera in order to ensure a supply of human cadavers for dissection, and were mobbed and sometimes murdered while their hospitals and schools of anatomy were stoned or burnt down.[18] And in 1900, when there was a brief outbreak of bubonic plague in Sydney, New South Wales, neighbours were encouraged to spy on neighbours – and the Chinese inhabitants, who were suspected as the source of the outbreak, were subjected to virulent campaigns of abuse and isolation, and forced to occupy tents on the beaches.[19]

3.1.4   Apart from epidemics, there have of course always been infectious diseases which have been endemic within a population, taking a steady toll of morbidity and mortality without any sudden or dramatic outbreaks of infection: leprosy, smallpox, tuberculosis, diphtheria, scarlet fever, and so on. In recent years, developments in medical science have succeeded in reducing these to almost negligible proportions, at all events in the developed countries. But for many centuries before that, their victims were apt to be ostracised, if not positively persecuted: even today, the word 'leper' is a synonym for a polluted outcast from society.

3.1.5   Clearly, it would not be safe ever to discount entirely the risk that an infectious disease – especially one that is perceived as presenting a serious threat, and more especially still one that lends itself to ready condemnation of those infected – will evoke among the general population, and the media of publicity, demands for protection of such intensity that it may become extremely difficult for governments – especially elected ones – not to offer them some gratification, even at the cost of severe injustice to those against whom the public outcry is directed, and the possible violation of their human rights.

3.1.6   As the World Health Organisation (WHO) puts it:

> *'Personal and public reaction to AIDS throughout the world has been of considerable depth and extent. Fear of AIDS and stigmatization of different groups (homosexual men, haemophiliacs, female prostitutes) have become common. Wherever those free from HIV feel threatened by*

those infected with HIV, especially where the latter form a defined group such as homosexuals and drug addicts, there may be calls for marking out and isolating those infected.

... As the toll of clinical disease rises, there will be increasing pressure on the authorities to take further action and adopt approaches that may or may not be effective or have any rational justification.'[20]

3.1.7   In fact, what is critical for any such infection is not whether it is endemic, epidemic, or (in the extreme case) pandemic, but how the infective vector travels from one person to another, for how long any given person is liable to remain infectious, and whether at any given time there are any known means either for protecting someone from the infection, or for combatting the infection once he or she has acquired it.

3.1.8   Here, AIDS bears little resemblance — with a single exception considered below — to most other previously known infectious diseases. Unlike their vectors, HIV is not transmitted through droplet infection, insect or other parasite infestation, polluted water or ordinary social contacts: AIDS is essentially a sexually, not a socially, transmitted disease. Where the incubation period — that is, the time between infection and the moment that the person begins to present identifiable symptoms — of most of the more common infective diseases is measured in days[21] or, at most, weeks, that for AIDS may be several years, during all of which time the carrier is potentially infectious. At present, there is no form of immunisation, and no known cure.

3.1.9   Moreover, people with this infection fall essentially into only three groups: the sexual partners of infected individuals, those who receive contaminated injections or transfusions, and the babies of infected women. In the developed countries, the second group is now composed largely of drug users who share syringes: the number of other members in that group who were previously at risk (people with haemophilia and other recipients of contaminated blood or blood products into their bloodstream) should be greatly reduced as all reasonable precautions are being taken to prevent their infection. The great majority of future patients will therefore acquire their infection through an act (their own, or that of someone close to them) which many people will condemn as wrong or immoral.

3.2 An analogy

3.2.1 Perhaps the closest historical analogy for AIDS is syphilis, during the four centuries or so between its appearance in Europe and the discoveries of a blood test for it, and a specific curative drug, by Wasserman and Ehrlich respectively. It may be helpful here to remind ourselves of the similarities between the two conditions, as well as the differences between them.

3.2.2 Among the similarities are the following:

- both conditions are sexually transmitted;

- both conditions can also be acquired by babies at birth, or through direct blood-to-blood contacts, e.g. during surgery;

- both conditions have a high ultimate mortality, preceded by a substantial period of severe suffering;

- in both cases the person (especially, in the case of syphilis, if female) may be unaware for many years that she has been infected;

- in both cases, the person will be infectious to others during parts of that period;

- both conditions are (or were at the relevant time) incurable.

3.2.3 The following appear to be the only substantial differences between the two conditions:

- syphilis often (but not always) gives some warning of its acquisition through a single 'primary' ulcer and/or a 'secondary' rash; AIDS may produce a non-specific 'glandular-fever-like' malaise at or about the time of sero-conversion, but this is recognised in only a minority of its cases; unlike most syphilitics, therefore, persons infected with HIV will only rarely have any warning that they may be infectious to others;

- in the case of AIDS, the median period from infection by HIV to the development of the full clinical syndrome seems at present to be around 7 to 8 years; for syphilis, it can be as long as 35 years from first infection to the manifestation of the neuro-psychiatric 'tertiary' stage.

3.2.4 In many respects, then, the two conditions have much in common. Certainly, for the best part of four centuries, syphilis was a major scourge, causing a great deal of suffering[22] – and indeed premature death – to untold numbers of people of both sexes,[23] and evoking public fears and condemnations very similar to those that AIDS does today.

3.2.5 There were many attempts in many countries to deal with the problem of syphilis – including some that were reminiscent of the worst of the mediaeval responses to 'plagues' of all kinds. But it may be interesting to note briefly how this problem was eventually dealt with in the United Kingdom. Between 1864 and 1869, three so-called Contagious Diseases Acts were passed, enabling suspected prostitutes in certain named garrison towns and ports to be detained, subjected to a statutory medical examination, and compulsorily treated while in detention. The scheme proved to be useless, and evoked much opposition, not least from the medical profession which had no desire to be cast in the role of a 'medical police': the Acts were eventually repealed in 1886. In 1916, a Royal Commission on Venereal Diseases instead recommended the setting-up of special clinics offering free treatment on an entirely voluntary basis, and guaranteeing complete anonymity and confidentiality – on the ground that the most successful policy for minimising the spread of such afflictions would be early detection, for which the voluntary and confidential co-operation of the patients themselves was essential.[24] This scheme was duly instituted, exists to this day, and has worked remarkably well.

3.3 Policy options

According to the World Health Organisation, no region of the world is now free from AIDS, and by October 1988 142 countries had already officially reported its presence.[25] With no vaccine or cure yet available, all governments are therefore now faced with the task of identifying and adopting measures which will hold out a realistic prospect of limiting its spread within their populations. For the purpose of considering their impact on human rights, such measures may be most conveniently grouped into three categories:

- measures which can have no adverse effect on the human rights of any individuals;

- measures which could have an adverse effect, but which can only be implemented with the explicit, free, and informed consent of the individual concerned;

- measures entailing some degree of direct or indirect compulsion.

3.3.1   *Measures without adverse effects*

These include:

- research into the pathophysiology of the disease, its modes of transmission, and the development of vaccines and curative drugs;

- ensuring the safety of blood for transfusions, blood products for use in treatment, semen for artificial insemination, and other cells, tissues and organs for transplantation;

- preventing the re-use of needles, syringes and other skin-piercing or invasive equipment without proper sterilisation;

- making safety devices, such as condoms and sterile syringes, more widely available, especially to people who practise high risk behaviour;

- health information, education and promotion programmes, directed either at the general public or to groups particularly at risk – such as prostitutes of either sex, their customers, drug misusers, and – in the developed countries – homosexual and bisexual men.

All these measures are strongly recommended by public health experts, including WHO.[26] None of them could adversely affect the human rights of anyone, and they need not therefore be further considered in this paper.

3.3.2   *Measures requiring explicit consent*

These include:

- the voluntary testing of individuals for HIV infection, either on an 'anonymous' basis (that is, without being required to give a true name, or any other identifying particulars), or with stringent safeguards for confidentiality;

- the counselling of individuals, both before and after they are tested,

- their voluntary treatment to mitigate the effects of infection, or to achieve modifications of their behaviour which they themselves desire.

These measures too are recommended by public health experts.[27] Provided that they are undertaken completely voluntarily – that is, after a full explanation of all the possible consequences, and with the explicit, free and informed consent of the person concerned, obtained without the application of any illicit pressures, whether in the form of promises or of threats – there can be no objection to them on human rights grounds, and they too need not therefore be further considered in this paper.

3.3.3 *Measures entailing compulsion*

3.3.3.1 Compulsion may take many different forms. The most obvious is the use, or the threat of use, of direct force. But making an act (e.g. refusal or failure to undergo an HIV test) criminal is also a form of compulsion; and so are express or implied threats of any other kind – such as that the person concerned will be deprived of some benefit if he or she does not submit to the desired procedure. It is this group of measures which carries clear risks of violations of human rights.

3.3.3.2 For the purposes of this paper, we shall ignore proposals so unrealistic that no rational government could consider them seriously – such as the proposal, allegedly once made by a politician in an unguarded moment, to 'shoot the queers';[28] excluding all foreigners from entry into a country; testing a nation's entire population;[29] or (as is reported to have been once suggested by a public health official) 'outlawing sexual intercourse between citizens and the rest of humanity, as it is only from foreigners that we get this disease'.[30] All such measures would of course constitute gross, and wholly unjustifiable, violations of human rights.

3.3.3.3   We are thus left with a group of measures, which may be feasible in practice and could therefore be realistically considered by public authorities, designed to impose some kinds of restriction on actual or potential HIV-seropositive persons in order to minimise the likelihood of their passing their infection on to others. These restrictions could be of several kinds, which we shall consider below.

3.3.3.4   But before any restriction can be imposed on anyone, one needs to identify the persons concerned. This can only be done by some kind of screening – either for one or more attributes regarded as indicators of *probable* infection, or by testing directly for *actual* infection. All these remaining measures therefore necessarily entail a direct or indirect assessment of the seropositivity of the persons concerned, and the reporting of the result to someone else – as, for example, by establishing registers of such persons, or making HIV infection a notifiable disease, or compulsorily tracing and informing their sexual partners.

3.3.3.5   Since it would never be possible in practice – let alone justifiable on either public health[31] or human rights grounds – to place restrictions on the entire population of even a small nation, such screening would need to concentrate on previously specified groups, as for example:

- persons thought to be at special risk of both acquiring the infection and passing it on to others, such as prostitutes of either sex, their customers, drug abusers, or homosexual or bisexual men;

- persons – whether citizens or aliens – seeking entry at a frontier, port, or airport;

- hospital patients;

- persons wishing to marry;

- prisoners;

- persons engaged in some specially sensitive occupations.

3.3.3.6   Among the restrictions which might be contemplated for those found to be HIV-positive might be:

- quarantine, isolation, or detention;

- refusal of entry to the country;

- exclusion from marriage, employment, housing, social services, attendance at educational or other establishments, or some other benefit.

3.4 Testing the legitimacy of policies

3.4.1 In the rest of this paper, we shall therefore consider the legitimacy, by reference to the international code of human rights law, of the various permutations and combinations of these measures in different circumstances.

3.4.2 We should, however, perhaps first remind ourselves that, where the code allows *any* restrictions of any of the human rights which it seeks to protect, such a restriction will only be considered justifiable if:

- it is 'provided by law'; and

- it is 'necessary in a democratic society'

- for the protection of a 'legitimate aim' which falls within one of the categories specifically listed in the relevant Article.

The second of these requirements in turn entails that:

- there must be a 'pressing social need'; and

- the restriction must be 'proportional' to that need, weighed both against its adverse effects on the persons on whom it is imposed, and against the public interest in the free exercise of the right concerned.

3.4.3 The first requirement – 'provided by law' – is the easiest to meet: all that is needed is that the State concerned should enact, by the procedures normally required for that purpose under its Constitution, legislation which satisfies the necessary criteria. These are that the law concerned must be sufficiently accessible, clear and precise for the ordinary individual to be able to regulate his or her conduct accordingly: he or she must be able – if necessary with appropriate advice – to foresee, to a degree that is reasonable in the circumstances, the consequences which a given action may entail.[32] For the purposes of this paper, we shall assume that any restriction on human rights imposed by public authorities for the purpose of limiting the spread of AIDS among their populations will satisfy this test. (If it does not, that will be the end of the matter: the restriction will be illegitimate under international human rights law.)

3.4.4 The next question will then be whether the restriction is designed to serve a 'legitimate aim' within one of the categories listed in the relevant Article, for the protection of which restrictions on the right under consideration may be allowed in appropriate circumstances. Among these categories there are only two that are relevant for our purposes: 'the protection of the rights and freedoms of others', and 'the protection of public health'.

3.4.5 Among 'the rights and freedoms of others', the only one that needs to be considered here – at least so long as there is no known cure for AIDS – is the human right to life. (There is also an independent right to 'the enjoyment of the highest attainable standard of physical and mental health' under Article 12 of the International Covenant on Economic, Social and Cultural Rights, and its equivalent under Article 11 of the European Social Charter, but for our purposes this may be subsumed into 'the protection of public health'.)

3.4.6 One might be forgiven for thinking that the right to life was in some sense paramount over all the other human rights protected by the code. But on closer analysis, such a ranking proves to be illusory. Human life is by its nature finite: the single human condition associated with 100% mortality is to be born into the world in the first place. At some point, everyone will die, and even the best-intentioned State cannot prevent this, whatever proportion of its resources – which are also finite – it applies to the prolongation of its inhabitants' lives. And while those inhabitants are alive, they have many other rights and freedoms which the State must respect and protect, and these too will make substantial calls on its finite resources. To take an extreme example: if the right to life were indeed paramount over all other human rights, the State would always be bound to use the most heroic and expensive measures to extend the lives of a few of its sickest members by just a few months – even at the cost, say, of depriving many of its children of the right to education.

3.4.7   Ultimately, therefore, the human right to life can impose on a State only the following obligations:

- not itself 'unlawfully' or 'arbitrarily'[33] to take or abbreviate the lives of any of its inhabitants within their natural span, e.g by 'extra-judicial executions' at the hands of State-encouraged or State-tolerated death squads;

- to establish and maintain laws and law enforcement agencies which will provide a reasonably effective deterrent against murder and manslaughter – but not, for example, to the point of providing personal bodyguards, for indefinite periods, to individuals who fear that their lives may be threatened by illegal organisations,[34] let alone installing a police state which will substantially abridge or deny the other human rights of the members of its society;

- to take what measures it reasonably can to prolong its inhabitants' lives where this can be done at a cost that is reasonable, both in resources and in terms of restrictions on other human rights.

3.4.8   A good example of the last of these is to be found in voluntary State-supported vaccination schemes designed to protect the health of society. In such cases, a State will be held to comply sufficiently with its obligation to protect the right to life if it establishes a system of control and supervision designed to reduce as much as possible the number of fatalities that could result from the scheme.[35]

3.4.9   Since AIDS, once the full clinical syndrome has developed, is almost invariably fatal, and since there is at present no known cure for it, every new infection with HIV is a potential fatality, and so threatens the right to life of the person newly infected. Accordingly, every measure which succeeds in reducing the spread of HIV infection will not only serve 'the protection of public health', but will automatically serve to protect the right to life. It follows that, in the rest of this paper, it will be enough to consider such measures under the aspect of the protection of public health, and we shall therefore not need to consider them separately from the point of view of the protection of the right to life, and so (with few exceptions) of 'the protection of the rights and freedoms of others'.

3.4.10   That will then leave, as the final question for testing the legitimacy of such measures, the proportionality of the balance between the benefits to be expected from them on the one hand, and on the other hand their adverse consequences for the persons concerned, as well as the public interest in the free exercise of the right that is being restricted – all these things being considered in the light of the degree and kind of 'pressing social need' presented to the government of the State concerned. This will therefore be the principal question to be considered, for each of the human rights concerned, in the remaining sections of this paper.

3.4.11   For the purposes of that exercise, any views already expressed by responsible and reputable public health experts, and by governments, on the utility of the measures concerned will clearly be important (though not necessarily conclusive). These will therefore be cited where they are known and appear to be relevant. However, it must be borne in mind that these views may yet change hereafter, in the light of advancing knowledge and experience of the public health aspects of AIDS.

3.4.12   Likewise, even though the international organs competent to interpret and apply human rights law do not follow a 'doctrine of binding precedent', any reported decisions which they have reached in this field will be of great importance. So far, no case specifically about AIDS has been decided or reported, and indeed there are only very few reported cases in which restrictions on human rights on the grounds of 'the protection of public health' have been considered. So far, therefore, one can only base one's views on the texts of the treaties themselves, and on interpretations of them which have been handed down in connection with problems that have arisen in adjoining fields. (As has already been explained, the bulk of these come from the European organs in Strasbourg, which have been interpreting and applying their regional Convention for more than 20 years longer than any of the other international institutions.) Those views must therefore also be subject to revision in the light of any future cases in which the international organs are called on to consider problems specifically related to AIDS.

4 *The Relevant Rights and Freedoms*

4.0   Since, as we have seen, some kind of screening for potential or actual HIV infection is in practice a necessary precondition for imposing on any members of a population, in support of measures designed to limit the spread of AIDS, any restrictions which might violate one or more of their human rights, we first need to consider the general implications of screening. Here, the major consideration will be the impact of this on the right to privacy, and we shall therefore deal with this right before we look at the other human rights which might be affected.

4.1 The right to privacy

4.1.0.1   There are two rather different definitions of this right in international law. Article 17 of the International Covenant on Civil and Political Rights says that:

> '*1. No one shall be subjected to arbitrary or unlawful interference with his privacy, family, home or correspondence, nor to unlawful attacks on his honour and reputation.*
>
> *2. Everyone has the right to the protection of the law against such interference or attacks.*'

Article 8 of the European Convention on Human Rights instead says that:

> '*Everyone has the right to respect for his private and family life, his home and his correspondence*'

and adds that:

> '*There shall be no interference by a public authority with the exercise of this right except such as is in accordance with the law and is necessary in a democratic society ... for the protection of health ...*'

4.1.0.2 The European Court of Human Rights has said that the right to privacy consists essentially of the right to live one's own life protected from arbitrary interference by public authorities.[36] However, both the Court and the Commission have held that the right to respect for private life does not end there. It also comprises the right to establish and develop relationships with other human beings, especially in the emotional sphere, for the development and fulfilment of one's own personality.[37]

4.1.0.3 Of the possible measures outlined above, several would necessarily entail interferences with the individual's right to privacy, which the State concerned would need to justify under the established criteria:

- mandatory testing for HIV seropositivity;

- the compulsory registration of persons considered as likely to be infected with HIV, but who have not been individually tested;

- the mandatory collection, storage and processing by public authorities of personal information about those who are suspected or have been tested;

- making AIDS, or HIV-seropositivity, a 'notifiable disease';

- the disclosure of test results, or of other personal information held, to third parties;

- the criminalisation of behaviour thought to be conducive to the spread of AIDS.

4.1.1 Mandatory testing

4.1.1.1 So far, the only reported cases about mandatory tests come from the European organs at Strasbourg. In connection with a blood test, the European Commission of Human Rights has said that 'a compulsory medical intervention, even if it is of minor importance, must be considered as an interference with [the right to respect for private life]'.[38] Since then, in a case called *Acmanne and others* v. *Belgium*,[39] the Commission has further said that requirements, enforceable by the criminal law, to undergo a tuberculin test or a diagnostic chest X-ray are interferences with this right.

4.1.1.2   In that case, the Commission found the interference justified, because 'the applicants had not produced evidence of disadvantages [of the test] comparable to the former ravages of tuberculosis, particularly among the deprived'. Accordingly, 'the individual had a social duty to defer to the general interest and not endanger the health of others where his life was not in danger'.

4.1.1.3   There are, however, some crucial differences between TB and AIDS. In the case of TB, one is dealing with an infectious disease for which there is a known cure. Mandatory screening for it is aimed at identifying patients in order that they may be treated, and so be cured themselves and at the same time cease to be a risk of infection to others. Such screening has no adverse consequences for the person being tested. Moreover, TB screening was for a long time recommended by public health experts, and proved highly efficacious in reducing the prevalence of the disease.[40] By contrast, in the case of AIDS there is so far no effective treatment or cure. A positive result can give the person concerned precious little help. On the contrary, it has the direst consequences: it will be perceived as an effective death warrant to be executed at some uncertain time in the future, with the likelihood of being shunned by family, friends, employers and others for the whole of the remaining time – that is, for life.

4.1.1.4   Moreover, public health experts appear so far to have been unanimous in rejecting *mandatory* HIV screening as an efficacious means for reducing the spread of this infection – except in the case of voluntary donors of blood, semen, or other cells, tissues or organs, and even then only with their informed consent, with counselling, and with an assurance of confidentiality, so that such screening effectively becomes voluntary.[41] In their view, efforts to *compel* testing would be counter-productive: knowledge that a test would be required would simply deter those who most need to be educated and counselled from seeking medical advice: HIV infection would effectively be 'driven underground', when the most pressing need is to bring it to the surface.[42]

4.1.1.5   As the World Health Organisation has put it:

> '*Routine screening of high-risk groups (homosexuals and heterosexuals with multiple sexual contacts and intravenous drug abusers), of other groups (military personnel, international travellers and hospital patients) and as a prerequisite for marriage is of little use in controlling or slowing down the AIDS epidemic.*'[43]

4.1.1.6   In any case, a negative HIV test gives no guarantee that the person tested is not a carrier of the virus: he or she might acquire the infection the following day, or might indeed have already become infected, but not yet have seroconverted.

4.1.1.7   Instead, public health experts recommend a less coercive, and in their view more efficacious, alternative, namely increasing the availability of *voluntary* testing, together with a broadly-based information and education campaign to encourage abandonment of high-risk behaviour. The purpose of this is to identify infected persons – who might not otherwise change their behaviour because they do not know they present a risk – so that they can be intensively counselled not to engage in behaviour that might be dangerous to others. As Dr. Jonathan Mann, the Director of WHO's Global Programme on AIDS has put it:

> '*In most instances, HIV transmission involves the behaviour of two persons; a change in behaviour of either the HIV-infected or the uninfected persons will be sufficient to prevent HIV transmission.*'[44]

4.1.1.8   The same view was expressed by the World Summit of Ministers of Health, attended by delegates from no fewer than 148 countries in London in January 1988:

> '*... the single most important component of national AIDS programmes is information and education because HIV transmission can be prevented through informed and responsible behaviour.*'[45]

4.1.1.9   There appears indeed to be some evidence to suggest that substantial behaviour changes have already occurred within the male homosexual community in the USA, the UK, and elsewhere as a result of the introduction of policies of this kind, and without any mandatory testing.[46]

4.1.1.10 It is also pertinent to note that the Committee of Ministers of the Council of Europe, explicitly taking into account the European Convention on Human Rights, has recommended that 'there should be no compulsory screening [for HIV infection] of the general population nor of particular population groups' and that 'health authorities should instead invest resources in the setting up of sites ... for voluntary testing ...'.[47]

4.1.1.11 In the light of all these considerations it seems unlikely, in present circumstances, that any scheme for mandatory screening would satisfy the test of being 'necessary in a democratic society' for the protection of public health: the interference with the right to privacy, and the severe adverse consequences which would flow from it to the individuals concerned, and to society at large through the limitation placed on the right to privacy, would appear to outweigh any benefits for public health which could reasonably be expected – if indeed there are any.

4.1.2 *Compulsory registration of suspected HIV carriers*

4.1.2.1 Manifestly, the entry of one's name on a register maintained by a public authority of what would effectively be regarded as a list of potential dangers to the community would be a grave violation of one's privacy – the more so as the overwhelming majority of the members of the category so included would appear there by reason of their suspected, or reported, or even actual, sexual activities or proclivities. In order for such a measure to be effective, it would need to be enforced by law – say, by placing prostitutes, their customers, or male homosexuals or bisexuals, under an obligation to register with the authorities, on pain of criminal sanctions if they do not; or by requiring anyone with knowledge of the name, address and activities of such a person to report that knowledge to a public authority, with similar sanctions.

4.1.2.2 It is not immediately obvious how such a law could be effectively enforced. However, even if it could, such a measure could never pass the stringent tests implied in the phrase 'necessary in a democratic society' without quite overwhelming evidence of its efficacy in public health terms, coming from reputable public health experts. So far as is known, no such evidence exists. The

State concerned would also need to show that no measures having less dramatically adverse consequences for the persons concerned, or for society generally, were available, or could be expected to have similarly beneficial results for public health. That burden too would be decidedly difficult to discharge.

4.1.3 *Mandatory collection and storage of information*

4.1.3.1 Schemes which include the mandatory collection, storage, and processing by a public authority of personal information about individuals suspected or tested for HIV infection (including, for example, test results, and answers to questions about sexual activities, partners, and drug use) would involve a clear interference with the right to privacy[48] – *unless* the information was protected by the strictest rules of medical confidentiality (that is, that any information so collected may only be released either anonymously, or with the explicit and informed consent of the person to whom it relates) or, better still, by complete anonymity at the time of collection, so that it could never be traced back to an identifiable individual.

4.1.3.2 In order to justify such an interference, the State concerned would need once again to establish proportionality with a legitimate aim. In this case, however, it is not immediately clear what the aim would be.

4.1.3.3 If the collection is made by reference to identifiable individuals, and its purpose is to impose restrictions on some or all of these, then its establishment and maintenance could only be justified if *both*:

- the obtaining of the information, by testing or by the creation of registers of potentially 'dangerous' individuals, could be justified in its own right – which, as we have seen, is unlikely to be the case; *and*

- the restrictions themselves could be justified independently – as to which, see the later Sections of this paper.

4.1.3.4 If, on the other hand, the only purpose is the compilation of statistical data in order to ascertain the prevalence, or study the epidemiology, of HIV infection, this can be achieved at least as well by the far less intrusive policy of using only anonymous samples. Public health experts are in any case agreed that the assurance of anonymity would be more conducive to securing compliance with testing schemes,[49] and so make the information more reliable.

4.1.3.5   In this context, one must remember that where the prevalence of a disease in a population is very low – as HIV infection still is in the great majority of countries – an accurate indication of the rate of its spread over time can only be obtained by testing very large numbers of individuals[50] whose selection for inclusion in the sample has been entirely random, without any bias for or against those who might have acquired the infection. Clearly, if it is known that the test results will be held by a public authority in identifiable form, this will deter some possible carriers from being tested: the sample will thereby become biased, the results will become unreliable, and the value of the entire exercise will be compromised.

4.1.3.6   By contrast, if one were for example to conduct an HIV test on a fraction of blood routinely taken from some groups of patients, with their consent, for other purposes, *and that fraction was so completely anonymised that it would be totally impossible to relate it back to its donor*, one could obtain much reliable information about prevalence, and so serve the interests of public health. Although there was a lack of candour, since the intended use of such a fraction had not been expressly disclosed to the patients – for fear of irrational refusals, and a consequent bias in the sample – it would be difficult to demonstrate that there had been any adverse effects on the human rights of anyone.[51]

4.1.3.7   However, as a general rule, it is probably true to say that the more sensitive is the information about identified or identifiable persons which the public authorities of a State seek to collect – e.g. about sexual practices, drug use, or the names of prior sexual partners or spouses – the greater is the potential for abuse and the stronger the objections on human rights grounds.[52]

4.1.4   *AIDS or HIV-seropositivity as a 'notifiable disease'*

4.1.4.1   A particular case of collecting and storing information is that of making AIDS or HIV infection a 'notifiable disease'. There are two possible variants of this. One is simply to require notification to a public authority of all cases of AIDS or HIV-positivity as and when they become known, without any identifying particulars from which the patients could be traced, or else subject to the strictest rules of medical confidentiality. The other is to require medical practitioners, by law, to report to a public authority all cases of the disease which they encounter among their patients, in what would otherwise be a breach of medical confidentiality – that is, *with* identifying particulars, and *without* adequate guarantees of confidentiality thereafter.

4.1.4.2   Here, precisely the same considerations apply as in the general case considered in the previous Section. If identifying details *are* to be recorded, that would be a clear interference with the right to privacy and would have to be specifically justified, in the face of the accumulating evidence that it would deter some – perhaps many – possible HIV carriers from coming forward to be tested, knowing that their condition, if they were found to be HIV-positive, would be *identifiably* reported to a public authority.[53]

4.1.4.3   However, if the entire scheme were subject to the strictest compliance with the general rules of medical confidentiality – or, better still, entailed only anonymous notification from the outset – there would be no obvious objections.

4.1.4.4   It is noteworthy, in this connection, that the Council of Europe's Committee of Ministers has said that:

> *'For the purpose of gaining insight into the epidemiology of HIV infection:*
> - *the reporting of AIDS cases in strict compliance with confidentiality regulations is strongly recommended;*
> - *where implemented, the reporting of seropositivity should also be carried out in strict compliance with confidentiality regulations.'*[54]

4.1.5   *Disclosure of information*

4.1.5.1   A policy permitting or requiring the disclosure of the results of HIV tests to third persons without the patient's consent, or which permits the improper discovery by third persons of those results, also amounts to an interference with privacy.[55]

4.1.5.2   In order to justify such a policy, the State concerned would need to show that it was necessary, in a democratic society, for the protection of the rights of others (e.g. the patient's sexual partner(s), or his or her medical attendant, dentist, or other health workers) or, more generally, for the protection of public health. However, the available evidence as to its likely efficacy suggests that it is not. Ever since special clinics were established at the beginning of this century to deal with sexually transmitted diseases, it has been recognised that a guarantee of confidentiality is an indispensable condition for encouraging people to seek treatment, and thus reduce the spread of these diseases.

4.1.5.3 Leading public health experts appear to agree that this is even more so in the case of AIDS. For example, the US Surgeon General puts it thus in his *Report on AIDS:*

> *'Because of the stigma that has been associated with AIDS, many afflicted with the disease or who are infected with the AIDS virus are reluctant to be identified with AIDS. Because there is no vaccine to prevent AIDS and no cure, many feel that there is nothing to be gained by revealing sexual contacts that might also be infected with the AIDS virus. When a community or a state requires reporting of those infected with the AIDS virus to public health authorities in order to trace sexual and intravenous drug contacts – as is the practice with other sexually transmitted diseases – those infected with the AIDS virus go underground out of the mainstream of health care and education. For this reason current health practice is to protect the privacy of the individual infected with the AIDS virus and to maintain the strictest confidentiality concerning his/her health records.'*[56]

4.1.5.4 It has sometimes been suggested that health workers might constitute a special case, since their contacts with HIV-infected patients will be more intimate than those of others, and will therefore expose them to a higher risk of acquiring the infection themselves. Though this is undoubtedly so, it is also the case that health workers are better placed than others to protect themselves: they are trained to use hygienic procedures, as well as gloves and other barriers, against the many infective agents by which they are surrounded throughout their professional lives. The hepatitis B virus, for example, is transmitted in very similar fashion to HIV, and health workers are routinely trained in the procedures needed to protect themselves against this organism. Worldwide, down to March 1988 (that is, during the 7 years that this disease has been known to exist) only 11 cases had been reported of health workers becoming infected with HIV from their patients.[57] Any general interference, for the supposed benefit of this group, with their patients' right of privacy – such as, for example, mandatorily testing for HIV every patient admitted to hospital – would therefore be quite disproportionate to the aim pursued, and so could not be justified.[58]

4.1.5.5 In fact, health experts have confirmed that, with proper counselling, most infected AIDS patients can be persuaded to inform their medical advisors, dentists, other health workers, and sexual partners voluntarily. This is also the expressed policy of the Committee of Ministers of the Council of Europe:

> '... patients should ... themselves be left to advise health staff of their seropositivity unless the patient has specifically authorised a doctor to pass on this information.'[59]

4.1.5.6 Breach of confidentiality might, however, be warranted in exceptional circumstances – where, for example, despite counselling and advice, the patient continues to have unprotected sexual intercourse with his or her partner, having been warned by the doctor both of the dangers of this, and of the doctor's intention to make the disclosure if the patient does not; or if the patient is a health worker and is consistently negligent in observing routine hygiene precautions, or fails to follow medical advice about his or her work.[60] If doctors are allowed to breach confidentiality in such circumstances, these would of course have to be defined with sufficient precision to comply with the requirement that the interference with privacy must be 'in accordance with the law'.

4.1.6 Creating new crimes

4.1.6.1 Two potential measures have sometimes been mooted as possible means of using the *criminal* law for preventing or inhibiting behaviour thought to be conducive to the spread of AIDS. These are:

- making it a specific criminal offence for an AIDS carrier knowingly or recklessly to infect others without their consent; and

- making male homosexual conduct a criminal offence where this is not already so.

4.1.6.2   The first of these would of course formally constitute an interference with the carrier's private life, but might be held to be justifiable on the grounds of the protection of public health, or of the rights and freedoms (and especially the right to life) of others, *provided* that the offence could be defined sufficiently precisely to meet the requirements of legal certainty and foreseeability. It is an elementary proposition not only of international human rights law,[61] but of virtually all domestic legal systems, that the ingredients of any criminal offence must be sufficiently precise for any person contemplating the commission of a particular act not to be in any doubt as to whether or not that act would be criminal.

4.1.6.3   Accordingly, the definition of any such offence would have to specify clearly how it is to be proved that:

- the accused knew that he or she was an actual carrier of HIV;

- the accused knew that his or her actual conduct carried a substantial risk of infecting another person;

- it was this conduct which in fact infected that other person;

- that other person did not consent to the risk of being infected.

To give just one example: what would be the position of someone who knows that he is HIV-positive and attempts, but fails, to protect his sexual partner because he has not fully understood all the requirements for 'safe sex' – or because he has used a condom which proves to be defective?

4.1.6.4   As for the criminalisation (or recriminalisation) of male homosexual conduct, it seems clear from the jurisprudence of the European Court of Human Rights that this could not be regarded as a justified interference with the right to respect for the private lives of homosexuals. In *Dudgeon* v. *United Kingdom*,[62] and most recently in *Norris* v. *Ireland*,[63] the Court has clearly held that no law prohibiting homosexual conduct in private between consenting males over the age of 21 can be justified in a democratic society.

4.1.6.5   In the Court's view, making such conduct a criminal offence – even if in practice no one is ever prosecuted under it – constitutes an interference with the right to respect for the private lives (which includes the sexual lives) of persons of homosexual orientation as it causes them fear, suffering, and psychological distress. Moreover, the Court found that such a wide law was not necessary in a democratic society either for the protection of morals, or for the protection of the rights and freedoms of others; any justifications for the prohibition were outweighed by the effects which they could have on the lives of homosexuals, and they were disproportionate to the aims sought to be achieved.

4.1.6.6   In the context of AIDS, the principal justification asserted for the imposition of a criminal sanction on all homosexual conduct would presumably not be – as it was in the cases of *Dudgeon* and *Norris* – the protection of public morals, but rather the protection of public health, as well as the protection of the rights and freedoms (including the right to life) of others. However, in order to succeed under this head, it would have to be established that the prohibition of male homosexual conduct alone – without any prohibition of the sexual activities, of all kinds, of the rest of society – would produce such a striking benefit in meeting the 'pressing social need' of limiting the spread of AIDS within the entire society that the adverse effects on *all* the homosexuals who would come within its ambit would be no more than proportionate to this legitimate aim.

4.1.6.7   Clearly, that proposition could not be established: such a prohibition would be disproportionate to the aim sought to be achieved because it would be far too broad. It would catch within its net not only those homosexuals who in fact present a risk to others, but also all those (today, since the advent of AIDS, probably the great majority) whose conduct – for example, by fidelity to a single partner, or by always taking all necessary prophylactic measures – made them no more of a risk to the rest of society than any heterosexual.

4.1.7   Summary

The conclusion, in the present section of this paper, that screening in both its possible forms – that is, the mandatory testing of any group of individuals, or the registration with a public authority of suspected HIV carriers as potentially 'dangerous' – would constitute violations of those persons' human right to privacy, and that such violations could not be justified as a matter of human rights law, in one sense disposes of any further questions of human rights which might arise from restrictive public health measures about AIDS: if it would not be legitimate to select individuals on whom to impose restrictions, then it would be totally arbitrary – and so a *fortiori* illegitimate – to impose restrictions on individuals who had *not* been subjected to any selection process.

Rather than content ourselves with that conclusion, however, we shall now proceed to consider separately the other human rights which might be abridged or denied through restrictions imposed by public health measures directed to the aim of limiting the spread of HIV infection.

4.2   The right to liberty and security

4.2.1   The rights to liberty and security of the person are protected, together and in virtually identical terms, in each of the major international human rights instruments. These all proclaim that:

> *'Everyone has the right to liberty and security of person'.*

Although the instruments do not themselves further define the term 'liberty' in this context, the European Court of Human Rights has expressed the view that it contemplates individual liberty in its classic sense: that is, the physical liberty of the person.[64] The concept of 'security', in this context, then means protection against arbitrary interference with this liberty.

4.2.2   The international instruments all go on to stipulate that any deprivation of liberty must be on grounds, and by procedures, established (or prescribed) by law. However, the European Convention on Human Rights goes further in that it sets out an exhaustive list of what the grounds of deprivation of liberty may be – and thereby, uniquely, forbids arrest or detention on any other ground, *even if* prescribed by law. The purpose of the guarantee of the right to liberty is, in the words of the European Court, to ensure that no one is deprived of his liberty 'arbitrarily'.[65] Indeed, the proposition that 'No one shall be subjected to arbitrary arrest or detention' is formulated as a separate component of the right to liberty and security in several of the other international instruments.[66]

4.2.3   In order to determine whether a person has been deprived of his or her liberty –

and hence whether these protections apply – regard must be had to the individual's concrete situation, and account must be taken of a whole range of criteria such as the type, duration, effects and manner of implementation of the measure in question.[67] The European Court has expressed the view that the difference between deprivation of liberty and restriction upon liberty is merely one of degree or intensity, and not one of nature or substance.

4.2.4 It is clear that deprivation of liberty is not confined to the classic forms of detention in a prison or a mental hospital, but may take other forms. To take two examples relevant for the purposes of this paper:

- The compulsory taking of a blood sample has been found to constitute a deprivation of liberty, however short.[68]

- Where the individual concerned was confined to a small area of an island, subjected to almost permanent supervision, and virtually deprived of the possibility of making social contacts, this has been held to amount to a deprivation of liberty. The Court in fact likened such a régime to an open prison.[69]

4.2.5 On the other hand, once there has been a lawful deprivation of liberty, mere modifications of the conditions of detention – such as isolation imposed on a prisoner as a disciplinary measure – will not be regarded as constituting independent deprivations of liberty.[70] Such treatment may, however, raise an issue of compliance with the right not to be subjected to inhuman or degrading treatment (see Section 4.9. below).

4.2.6 Based on this jurisprudence, the following possible public health measures would appear to involve a deprivation of liberty:

- compulsory blood tests;

- compulsory quarantine, e.g. by enforced confinement or isolation in a hospital or a hospice;

- compulsory internment in a colony removed from the rest of society (along the lines of a leper colony).

4.2.7   In order to be justified, such measures would then have to satisfy the test that they are not arbitrary, but are taken on a ground, and in accordance with a procedure, established (or prescribed) by law. As we have seen, only the European Convention specifically and exhaustively enumerates the grounds on which a person may lawfully be deprived of his or her liberty. However, in interpreting and applying the other international human rights instruments it is likely that the bodies charged with that task will have regard to these specific grounds in determining whether a deprivation of liberty has been 'arbitrary'.

4.2.8   One of the grounds on which a person may lawfully be deprived of his or her liberty under the European Convention is 'for the prevention of the spreading of infectious diseases'.[71] It is presumably this ground which would be invoked in support of any of the measures mentioned above. This ground of detention has not yet been the subject of specific interpretation, but the very similar clause authorising detention on grounds of mental illness has been interpreted and applied in several cases in considerable detail, as have other parallel clauses in this Article. The jurisprudence relating to these will therefore furnish some indication of how the ground relating to infectious diseases would be interpreted and applied.

4.2.9   Where – as here – detention is authorised as being for a particular purpose (as, for example, bringing an individual before the courts, securing his deportation, or educational supervision), the European Commission and the Court have expressed the view that the detention must be 'necessary' for that purpose.[72] In fact, these clauses do not expressly refer to necessity, but the Strasbourg organs have taken the view that, since they are exception clauses, they must be strictly interpreted, and no criteria other than those mentioned in them may be the basis of any restriction of the right to liberty and security of the person.[73]

4.2.10   In the case of the detention of a 'person of unsound mind', the Court has held that three minimum conditions must be satisfied for the detention to be lawful:

- except in emergency cases, a true mental disorder must be reliably established before a competent authority on the basis of *objective medical expertise;*

- the mental disorder must be of a kind or degree *warranting compulsory medical confinement;* and

- the validity of continued confinement must depend on the *persistence* of such a disorder.[74]

4.2.11 There is no obvious reason why the detention of a person for the express purpose of preventing the spread of an infectious disease should be subject to any less stringent conditions than detention on the grounds of mental illness. In order, therefore, for the measures under consideration to be justifiable, it would appear that the State concerned would have to establish that:

- compulsory blood testing was necessary for preventing the spread of HIV infection;

- in the case of detention, both that the individual concerned had the infection and that his or her detention was necessary for preventing its spread.

4.2.12 The views of public health experts about the efficacy of compulsory blood testing as a measure to prevent the spread of HIV infection have been set out in Section 4.1.1. above, and do not need to be repeated here: suffice it to say that they make it extremely doubtful that such a measure could be justified under international human rights law.

4.2.13 As to whether detention of any kind is warranted to control or prevent the spread of AIDS, WHO has expressed the firm view that it is not:

'There is no public health rationale to justify isolation [or] quarantine, ... based solely on the fact that a person is suspected or known to be HIV infected. The modes of HIV transmission are limited (sex, blood, mother-to-child) and HIV spreads almost entirely through identifiable behaviours and specific actions which are subject to individual control. In most instances, the active participation of **two** *people is required for HIV transmission, such as in sexual intercourse and in sharing contaminated needles or syringes. ...*

> *HIV infection is **not** spread through casual contact, routine social contact in schools, the workplace or public places, nor through water or food, eating utensils, coughing or sneezing, insects, toilets or swimming pools.'*[75]

4.2.14   WHO has in fact gone further. It has stated, as part of its recommended strategy for the prevention of the spread of AIDS, that:

> *'... persons suspected or known to be HIV-infected should remain integrated within society to the maximum possible extent and be helped to assume responsibility for preventing HIV transmission to others. Exclusion of persons suspected or known to be HIV-infected would be unjustified in public health terms and would seriously jeopardise educational and other efforts to prevent the spread of HIV.'*[76]

4.2.15   The Committee of Ministers of the Council of Europe has also recommended that:

> *'Public health regulatory measures such as ... restriction of movement or isolation of carriers should as a general rule not be introduced on a compulsory basis'.*[77]

4.2.16   Equally, there would appear to be no public health justification for a policy of compulsory segregation or isolation of prisoners who are known or suspected to be HIV-seropositive or who have AIDS, either in a separate unit or in single cells.[78] However, in the light of the view expressed by the European Commission of Human Rights that restrictions imposed on a prisoner's liberty are not to be considered as independent deprivations of liberty, such measures do not fall to be considered under the right to liberty. They may, on the other hand, be open to challenge on the ground that they amount to inhuman or degrading treatment – as to which, see Section 4.9 below.

4.2.17   To all this, there may be an exception in the case of a genuine emergency – for example if someone known to be, or suspected on cogent grounds of being, infected with HIV is found bleeding copiously and so presents an acute risk of infecting others, and is unable to take care of him or herself.

4.2.18   Another exception might be conceivable in the case of a person so disturbed or embittered by the knowledge of HIV-seropositivity that, despite intensive counselling, he or she insists on deliberately infecting others.

4.2.19   In either of these cases, such a person's detention might be justified, in the one case until the immediate emergency is over, and in the other until there is no further risk of conduct likely to infect others. However, it should be noted that in the case of *any* detention, all the relevant international instruments require a strict judicial control: the detainee must be 'entitled to take proceedings' before a court in which 'the lawfulness of his detention' can be decided 'without delay' (or 'speedily'), and his release can be ordered if the detention is not lawful.[79]

4.2.20   The European Court of Human Rights has held that, where the detention is for an indeterminate period – as in the case of mental patients,[80] or persons liable to recall after a sentence of imprisonment[81] – this gives the detainee a right to regular and periodic *judicial* reviews in order to ascertain whether the reasons for his or her detention continue to be satisfied, and accordingly whether the detention continues to be lawful. If it is not, the tribunal itself must have the power to order the detainee's release.

4.2.21   Accordingly, in either of the cases outlined above where an initial detention might be lawful, its continued lawfulness would depend on the right of the detainee to have access to a judicial tribunal which has the power to determine independently whether the initial grounds for the detention persist, and to order his or her release if they do not.

4.3   The right to freedom of movement

4.3.1   Freedom of movement comprises an interrelated cluster of rights: the right to enter a country; the right of abode and movement within a territory; freedom from expulsion; and the right to leave a country. Each of these applies differently to nationals of the State concerned and to aliens (i.e. non-nationals) and each of them is subject to different incidents.

In the present context, we are concerned with the first three, in order to assess the extent to which, if at all, a State might legitimately impose controls on entry into its country of those who are HIV-positive, restrict their movement within the country, or permit or require their expulsion from it.

4.3.2 Taking first the right to enter a country, this is defined in similar terms in each of the relevant international instruments. In the European Convention on Human Rights, the formulation is this:

> '*No one shall be deprived of the right to enter the territory of the State of which he is a national.*'[82]

This right of *entry* is clearly confined to nationals of the State concerned: nowhere in any international human rights treaty has any State accepted an express obligation to allow aliens to enter its territory.

4.3.3 For nationals, the freedom to enter is absolute and not subject to any restrictions. It could not, therefore, be legitimate for a State to make the entry into the country of its own returning nationals conditional on their taking an HIV test, let alone on obtaining a negative result.

4.3.4 By contrast, States enjoy a wide discretion about the entry of aliens. The choice of grounds for exclusion is largely a matter for each State to decide upon. This does not, however, mean that there are no restrictions on a State's ability to control entry for purposes of work, travel, or immigration. Rules of international law have made a limited impact on this broad power. So, for example, it can be said that the State's freedom of decision is limited by the principle of non-discrimination on racial grounds, and by the rule forbidding the return of refugees to a place where they fear persecution.[83]

4.3.5 For many States, there will be further restrictions deriving from treaty obligations. In the European context, for instance, all EEC nationals are accorded certain rights of access to other member states of the Community, and there is also a European Convention on Establishment designed to facilitate entry for the purpose of temporary visits, travel, and prolonged or permanent residence.[84]

4.3.6 Beyond this, the refusal of entry to aliens may well, in particular cases, interfere with their enjoyment of other rights guaranteed to them under international human rights law. Thus, for example, it may result in the separation of a husband and wife, or a parent and his or her dependants. In such cases, it would constitute an interference with the right to respect for family life which would have to be strictly justified by the State concerned as being 'necessary' for one of the specified purposes.

4.3.7 It is not the case, therefore, that the entry of *all* aliens into a country could be made contingent upon production of a certificate of freedom from HIV infection, or submission to an HIV test. Such a requirement could only be imposed in such cases if the State could establish that it was necessary, in a democratic society, for the protection of public health.

4.3.8 As to that, WHO has stated that:

> '*Since HIV infection is already present in every region and in virtually every major city in the world, even total exclusion of all travellers (foreigners and citizens travelling abroad) cannot prevent the introduction and spread of HIV.*'[85]

It goes on to point out that *hundreds of millions* (emphasis in original) of persons cross international borders each year, by boat, air, rail, motor vehicle and foot, and to draw attention to the immense problems which any screening programme for international travellers would present.

4.3.9 To this, the Committee of Ministers of the Council of Europe has added:

> '*In the light of present knowledge, discriminatory measures such as control at borders ... should not be introduced as they are not justified either scientifically or ethically.*'[86]

4.3.10 Turning to the freedom to choose a residence within the territory of a State and to move about freely within that State, the International Covenant on Civil and Political Rights provides, in language similar to that of the other international instruments, that:

> *'Everyone lawfully within the territory of a State shall, within that territory, have the right to liberty of movement and freedom to choose his residence.'*[87]

4.3.11 This right is guaranteed to nationals and aliens alike, but may be restricted on the usual grounds, including public health. It complements the protection afforded by the right to liberty of the person which we considered in the last Section. If, for example, a requirement to reside within a specified area did not in itself amount to a deprivation of liberty, it might well constitute a restriction on the right to movement. Indeed, the European Commission of Human Rights so found in an inter-State case concerning alleged restrictions imposed on the movement of Greek Cypriots in order to prevent them from moving freely outside villages in the north of Cyprus.[88]

4.3.12 As before, any such restriction would have to be strictly justified as being necessary in a democratic society for the protection of public health. However, public health experts have counselled against the introduction of such measures, thereby calling their necessity into question. The Committee of Ministers of the Council of Europe, for example, has said that:

> *'Public health regulatory measures such as ... restriction of movement of ... carriers, should as a general rule not be introduced on a compulsory basis.'*[88]

4.3.13 It is interesting to note, in this connection, that a French official circular on the medical examination of aliens[90] prescribes that HIV-seropositivity must not constitute grounds for refusal to grant authorisation to reside in France.

4.3.14 The protection against expulsion from a country afforded by international human rights law is rather more limited; it differs, moreover, in certain significant respects as between the various treaties. The European Convention on Human Rights and the American Convention on Human Rights both expressly prohibit the expulsion of nationals. In the words of the European Convention:

> *'No one shall be expelled, by means either of an individual or of a collective measure, from the territory of the State of which he is a national.'*[91]

This prohibition is absolute: no breach of it can be justified on any ground.

By contrast, the Covenant only says that:

> *'No one shall be arbitrarily deprived of the right to enter his own country.'*[92]

4.3.15   The protection afforded to aliens is of a different kind. Their 'collective' expulsion is absolutely prohibited by the European and American Conventions on Human Rights and by the African Charter, but none of the treaties affords any equivalent protection to *individual* aliens. However, apart from the European Convention, they all provide that – in the words of the International Covenant on Civil and Political Rights:

> *'An alien lawfully in the territory of a State Party to the present Covenant may be expelled therefrom only in pursuance of a decision reached in accordance with law ...'*[93]

The Covenant alone goes on to call for two additional procedural safeguards: the opportunity for the alien to submit reasons against his expulsion, and to have his or her case competently reviewed – 'except where compelling reasons of national security' (not, be it noted, public health) 'otherwise require'.

4.3.16   It would therefore seem that the following forms of expulsion, on the ground of AIDS or HIV-positivity, would be illegitimate under these provisions:

- the *arbitrary* expulsion of a citizen by any State Party to the International Covenant on Civil and Political Rights or the African Charter;

- *any* expulsion of a citizen by any State Party to either the European or the American Convention on Human Rights;

- the *collective* expulsion of aliens by a State Party to any of the three regional treaties;

- the *individual* expulsion of any alien by any State Party to the Covenant, the American Convention or the African Charter otherwise than 'in accordance with the law' and, in the case of a State Party to the Covenant, if he or she has not had the opportunity to submit reasons against the expulsion to a competent authority.

4.4 The right to marry and found a family

4.4.1 This right is guaranteed in virtually identical terms in the various international human rights treaties. Article 12 of the European Convention on Human Rights is illustrative:

> *'Men and women of marriageable age have the right to marry and to found a family, according to the national laws governing the exercise of this right.'*

4.4.2 On first reading, this provision might appear to afford 'national laws' an unlimited scope to impose conditions on this right. However, both the European Court of Human Rights and the Commission have made it clear that this is not so. Emphasising that the role of national law is merely to 'govern the exercise' of the right, they have held that it must not interfere with the substance of the right itself.[94]

4.4.3 National law may therefore lay down formal rules about matters such as notice, publicity, and the formalities whereby a marriage is solemnised. It may also lay down rules of substance based on generally recognised considerations of public interest, such as those relating to capacity, consent, and prohibited degrees of consanguinity.[95] However, it must not 'restrict or reduce the right in such a way or to such an extent that the very essence of the right is impaired'.[96]

4.4.4 The Court has also imported into Article 12 (where it is not in fact explicitly stated) the familiar test of 'necessity', holding that a measure which *does* affect the very essence of the right to marry must, in order to be justified, be proportionate to the legitimate aim pursued.[97] Even the imposition of a delay on the exercise of the right to marry has been held to constitute a substantial injury to the substance of this right.[98]

4.4.5 A policy of *mandatory* premarital HIV-testing, coupled with a denial of a marriage licence if either person proved to be positive, would therefore clearly be a measure interfering with the substance of the right to marry, as indeed would any prohibition of marriage for persons known, or suspected of being, HIV-positive. The question would then arise whether such a policy could be justified as being 'necessary' to reduce either the sexual or the perinatal transmission of the HIV virus. Although these might well be regarded as legitimate aims, it seems exceedingly doubtful whether preventing HIV-infected persons from marrying would be an effective means for achieving them.

4.4.6 In the first place, for many people today not being married is no bar to sexual activity with others; it may, on the contrary, simply encourage promiscuity. Even where there are ample opportunities for marriage, a substantial proportion of sexual activity takes place outside it; with marriage barred for some, that proportion could only increase, and probably involve more sexual partners.

4.4.7 Nor is there any reason to suppose that prohibiting marriage would be an effective means of preventing the transmission of the HIV virus to children. An increasing number of them today are born out of wedlock; indeed, measures have already had to be taken, at both national and international levels, to ensure that they are not discriminated against by comparison with children born in wedlock.[99] Moreover, there is evidence that the great majority of children infected with HIV are born to unmarried parents.[100]

4.4.8 WHO appears to have come to the same conclusion:

> *'Routine screening ... as a prerequisite for marriage is of little use in controlling or slowing down the AIDS epidemic.'*[101]

4.4.9 There are, moreover, less coercive and more effective alternative means to achieve both these ends, and this casts further doubt on the proportionality of such a measure.

4.4.10 A policy of requiring both parties to submit to a pre-marital AIDS test, informing the prospective spouse of the result (even without the other's consent), counselling about risk-reduction behaviour, and then issuing the marriage licence – regardless of the test result – may also be objectionable on human rights grounds, but for a different reason: it may well constitute an unjustified interference with the right to privacy of each of the prospective spouses, by requiring disclosure of the test results to the other without consent (see Section 4.1.5 above).

4.4.11 A law, on the other hand, requiring that each couple seeking a marriage licence be informed about HIV infection and risk-reduction behaviour, and offered the antibody test on a voluntary basis, would not appear to pose any human rights problems.

4.4.12 One of the most serious questions which arises in the context of AIDS is whether it could ever be justifiable for a government to adopt a policy which imposes restrictions on procreation for those identified as HIV-positive.

4.4.13 The wording of the international provision about 'the right to found a family' makes it clear that it too must be read subject to the same qualifications as those outlined above for the right to marry – namely that national laws may regulate the exercise of this right, but may not impair its substance. Clearly, therefore, public authorities would not be entitled to interfere with the founding of a family by, for instance, adopting a policy of ordering mandatory abortions or sterilisations – unless this was 'necessary' in order to achieve a legitimate aim, and strictly proportional to it.

4.4.14 Such a policy would presumably have the two-fold aim of seeking to protect the health of both the mother and the unborn children. While these might be legitimate aims, it seems clear that the policy would in fact be quite unjustifiable for seeking to achieve them, for the following reasons.

4.4.15 As regards the health of the prospective mother, it appears to be the case that the immune system weakens during pregnancy, and physicians are therefore concerned that pregnancy may increase the risk that women who are already infected with HIV will develop the full clinical AIDS syndrome. However, the need to protect the person concerned from herself could not be considered to be of sufficient weight to justify a measure of this nature, at all events in the case of an individual of full age and in possession of her mental faculties.[102]

4.4.16 As for the unborn child, perinatal transmission of HIV has been found to occur during pregnancy, delivery, and perhaps also soon after birth. The extent of the risk of transmission by these means is not yet known with any certainty.[103] However, even if it proved to be high, this could not justify such gross violations of human rights – reminiscent of some of Hitler's concentration camps – as *compulsory* abortions or sterilisations, contrary to the woman's expressed wishes,[104] any more than one could ever attempt to justify these in cases of genetically transmitted diseases.

4.5 The right to work

4.5.1 Several of the international instruments[105] declare that 'Everyone has the right to work'. Perhaps understandably, the precise meaning of this formulation remains controversial: commentators from socialist countries which maintain a planned economy say that it means that the State has an obligation to provide employment for every able-bodied adult among its inhabitants; commentators who support free-market economies say that the obligation is purely negative, in the sense that the State may not *prevent* any of its inhabitants from seeking or entering gainful employment.

4.5.2 For the purposes of this paper, it is fortunately unnecessary to enter into this controversy, since the relevant instruments[106] immediately proceed to say something like:

> *'Everyone has the right to the opportunity to gain his living by work which he freely chooses or accepts,'*

and add an obligation on the State to 'take appropriate steps to safeguard this right', or to 'protect [it] effectively'.

4.5.3 The UN Committee on Economic, Social and Cultural Rights, interpreting the provisions of the relevant International Covenant, has emphasised that an effective guarantee against arbitrary dismissal is an integral element of the right to work.[107] Interpreting the analogous provision in the European Social Charter, the Committee of Experts at Strasbourg has expressed the view that it is closely bound up with the eradication of all forms of discrimination in employment.[108] Thus, for example, the Committee has stated that a requirement that married women cannot enter the civil service, and that female civil servants should resign on marriage, is incompatible with this provision.[109]

4.5.4 However, some forms of discrimination in this field must clearly be permissible: there is nothing wrong, for example, in refusing to employ, or in dismissing, a schoolteacher who cannot read or write, or a chauffeur without a driving licence. The question must always be whether the ground for the discrimination is *objectively* relevant for the efficient and proper performance of the duties of the employment.

4.5.5 It follows that, if an applicant for a job were refused employment, or an employee were dismissed, solely on the ground that he or she was – or was suspected of being – HIV-positive, this would constitute an interference with his or her right to work unless it could be established that the absence of infection was a *bona fide* and *necessary* occupational qualification, or that the infection would clearly and substantially affect job performance.

4.5.6 For example, there might be no interference with the right to work if someone who was HIV-positive were not employed in a position requiring travel to countries which bar those so infected. Nor might there be such an interference if persons were not employed because they were already displaying some symptoms of fully developed AIDS, and their prognosis was such that they would either not be in the position long enough, or not be in sufficiently good health, to be able to carry out the normal duties of the employment. However, in any such case the situation would be no different than if such persons were suffering from any other disease having the same effect on their performance at work. As WHO and the International Labour Organisation (another specialised agency of the United Nations) have pointed out:

'Pre-employment HIV/AIDS screening as part of the assessment of fitness to work is unnecessary and should not be required. ...

There should be no obligation of the employee to inform the employer regarding his or her HIV/AIDS status.'

4.5.7 At least one major group of employers in the UK, with 5,000 members, has likewise concluded that:

'the many and serious limitations of pre-employment screening and the problems such a policy would present for a company will ... far outweigh any apparent benefits to an employer.'

Such a policy would:

- have a 'devastating' impact on an individual who has a positive test result;

- make recruitment more expensive and lead to delays in making appointments;

- undermine action by a company to reassure existing employees concerning safety and infection at the workplace.[111]

4.5.8 As for overt HIV-related symptoms manifesting after someone has been employed, WHO and ILO have this to say:

'If fitness to work is impaired by HIV-related illness, reasonable alternative working arrangements should be made. ...

HIV infection is not a cause for termination of employment. As with many other illnesses, persons with HIV-related illnesses should be able to work as long as medically fit for available, appropriate work.'[112]

4.5.9 Next, the question arises whether the risk of HIV infection leading to neuro-psychiatric disorders might be a sufficient reason for not employing infected persons in some exceptionally sensitive occupations such as train drivers or commercial pilots, on the ground that their faculties might become impaired and so put at risk other people's lives. Here, WHO has come to the following conclusions:

'... governments, employers and the public can be assured that based on the weight of available scientific evidence, otherwise healthy HIV-infected individuals are no more likely to be functionally impaired than uninfected persons. Thus, HIV screening would not be a useful strategy to identify functional impairment in otherwise healthy persons. Furthermore, there is no evidence that HIV screening of healthy persons would be useful in predicting the onset of functional impairment in persons who remain otherwise healthy.'[113]

4.5.10 Nor, on present evidence, do there appear to be any tenable grounds for restricting the involvement of those who are HIV-positive in the preparation or distribution of food. WHO has stated authoritatively that:

'HIV infection is not spread through water or food, [or] eating utensils.'[114]

4.5.11 The question then arises as to what extent, if any, measures may be taken which would interfere with an AIDS patient's right to work where his or her ability to perform the work in question is not at issue. Here, the analysis is a familiar one. Any restriction or limitation on the right to work must be prescribed by law, and be necessary in a democratic society for one of the specified purposes.[115]

4.5.12 In the context of AIDS, there is – among 'the protection of the rights and freedoms of others' – a particular purpose for which restrictions might be imposed on the right to work, namely the right of all workers to 'safe and healthy working conditions'.[116] Could this be invoked to justify refusing to employ, or dismissing, someone who is HIV-positive (or who refuses to reveal whether he or she is HIV-positive), on the ground that his or her presence constitutes a danger to their fellow workers?

4.5.13 Based on the views of public health experts, the short answer would seem to be no: such a measure would not meet the test of necessity. WHO and other public health experts have emphasised that there is no risk of infection where there is no direct contact with the blood, semen, or vaginal secretions of infected individuals. Few jobs outside the provision of health services involve contact with these, and other employees are therefore safe from infection whilst at work. To quote WHO:

> *'HIV infection is not spread through casual contact [or] routine social contact in ... the workplace.'*
>
> *'In the vast majority of occupations and occupational settings, work does not involve a risk of acquiring or transmitting HIV between workers, from worker to client, or from client to worker.'*[118]

4.5.14 The risk of ordinary employees coming into contact with such infected body fluids is likely to arise only from accidents and their treatment. According again to the public health experts, in a situation requiring first aid the standard precautions taken to reduce the risk of transmitting other blood-borne infections, including hepatitis B, will be equally effective against the AIDS virus.[119]

4.5.15 It is significant that in its recommendations for the formulation of a public health policy on AIDS, the Committee of Ministers of the Council of Europe has stated:

> *'In the light of present knowledge, discriminatory measures such as ... exclusion of carriers from ... employment ... should not be introduced as they are not justified either scientifically or ethically.'*[120]

It will be observed that this statement makes no exceptions for any particular kind of employment.

4.5.16 Finally, then, the question again arises whether health workers should be treated as a special case. We have already (in Section 4.1.5.) considered the special risks to which they may be exposed in *acquiring* the HIV infection: we must now consider the risks of their *transmitting* it.

4.5.17 Clearly, those who are routinely involved in invasive procedures – for example, medical and dental surgeons, nurses inserting cannulae or even just giving injections or taking blood samples – present a special risk of transmitting HIV to their patients if they themselves carry it, *and* if they do not observe the routine precautions designed to prevent *any* blood-borne infections from which they suffer from being so transmitted.

4.5.18 However, health workers are themselves uniquely aware of this risk and how it is best met – e.g. by withdrawing from particular aspects of their work which present it – and are generally highly responsible people. Indeed, there is not a single reported case of a health worker infecting a patient with HIV.[121] Accordingly, the circumstances in which it would be justified to interfere with the right to work of an HIV-infected health worker would have to be quite exceptional – e.g. if he or she were consistently negligent in observing the routine precautions, or failed to follow medical advice about their work.

4.6 The right to education

4.6.1 In defining 'the right of everyone to education', the International Covenant on Economic, Social and Cultural Rights makes it clear that *access* to education is an integral part of this right. The second paragraph of the relevant Article[122] provides that primary education shall be available free to all, that secondary education shall be made generally available and accessible to all, and that higher education shall be made equally accessible to all, on the basis of capacity.

4.6.2 The European Convention on Human Rights formulates the right to education in negative terms:

> 'No person shall be denied the right to education.'[123]

Interpreting this provision, the European Court of Human Rights has held that what is here guaranteed to persons subject to the State's jurisdiction is the right, in principle, to avail themselves of the means of instruction existing at a given time. In the Court's words, this provision guarantees

> 'the right of access to educational institutions existing at a given time'.[124]

4.6.3 Despite the apparently unqualified nature of the right to education, the European Court has expressed the view that this right, by its very nature, calls for regulation by the State: regulation which may vary in time and place according to the needs and resources of the community and of individuals. The Court has stressed, however, that such regulation must not injure the substance of the right, nor conflict with other rights enshrined in the Convention.[125]

4.6.4   Thus, for example, the Court found a breach of the right to education in circumstances where a child was suspended from school because of his and his parents' refusal to accept that he receive, or be liable to receive, corporal punishment. The Court held that a condition of access to an educational establishment which conflicted with another right enshrined in the Convention (in this case, the parents' right to respect for their philosophical convictions) could not be described as reasonable.[126]

4.6.5   For this purpose, the concept of 'reasonableness', like that of 'necessity', requires that the measure be both for a legitimate purpose and proportionate to the achievement of that purpose. A health policy prohibiting children infected with HIV from attending school would clearly constitute an interference with their right to education. In the light of the European Court's case law, such a measure could therefore only be justified if the interference was 'reasonable' in this sense.

4.6.6   The reasonableness of a general policy of exclusion of HIV carriers from school is highly questionable. Public health experts have been unanimous in stating that, on all present evidence, there is no risk of transmitting HIV in schools. To quote WHO:

> 'HIV infection is **not** spread through ... routine contact in schools' *(emphasis in original).*[127]

They state further that (as in the case of accidents occurring at the workplace) accidents at school – where, for example, an infected child is cut, sick, or incontinent – can be dealt with safely by following standard hygiene procedures.

4.6.7   Accordingly, they recommend that the fact of infection with HIV should not be a factor taken into account by education authorities in discharging their duties concerning school admissions, transfers, attendance, or their powers of exclusion from school.

4.6.8   The Committee of Ministers of the Council of Europe has made the following recommendation in this regard:

> *'In the light of present knowledge, discriminatory measures such as exclusion of carriers from school ... should not be introduced as they are not justified either scientifically or ethically.'*[128]

4.6.9 There may, conceivably, be some exceptional cases, as for example children who are so developmentally delayed or neurologically handicapped as to lack control of their body secretions. In such cases, it might be legitimate to take this fact into account, together with known information about HIV serological status, when assessing the child's educational needs.[129]

4.7 The right to social security, assistance, and welfare

4.7.1 Under the International Covenant on Economic, Social and Cultural Rights, the States Parties 'recognise the right of everyone to social security, including social insurance'.[130] The circumstances in which this security is to be provided are not, however, there specified. Nor have they yet been articulated by the competent international supervisory body established under the Covenant.

4.7.2 The European Social Charter, on the other hand, is much more specific in this regard. Under the Charter, the right to social security comprises four distinct rights. Of these, we are here concerned with three: the right to social security; the right to social and medical assistance; and the right to benefit from social welfare services.

4.7.3 As regards the first, the Charter provides that:

> *'All workers and their dependants have the right to social security.'*[131]

In order to make this right effective, States Parties have an obligation to establish or to maintain a system of social security.[132] Further, the system must be at least equal to that required for the ratification of ILO Convention No. 102 Concerning Minimum Standards of Social Security.[133] This requirement entails, *inter alia*, that a State must have a system which provides benefits in respect of at least three of the following:

- sickness;

- unemployment;

- old age;

- employment injury;

- maternity;

- invalidity;

- survivorship.

It follows – and indeed the European Committee of Experts charged with supervising the implementation of the Charter has observed in interpreting this provision[134] – that a system may be a genuine system of social security even though some risks (e.g. sickness and maternity benefits) are not covered.

4.7.4   The question then arises whether a government could legitimately stipulate that, if employees were dismissed because they had AIDS or took sick leave because of sickness attributable to AIDS, they could be denied unemployment or sickness benefits to which they would otherwise become entitled. It seems clear that it could not. The guarantee applies to 'all' workers, and the Preamble to the Charter states that social rights should be secured without discrimination. Accordingly, if a social security system provides for the payment of benefits in case of unemployment or sickness, it could not exclude people with AIDS from that protection.

4.7.5   To do so would constitute an interference with the individual's enjoyment of this right, which would have to be justified as being necessary in a democratic society for the protection of the rights and freedoms of others or for the protection of public health.[135] It is not evident how this exacting test could be met, as there is no apparent link between curtailing the rights of people with AIDS to social security and enhancing the protection of the rights and freedoms of others, or the protection of public health.

4.7.6 Turning to the second component of the right to social security, the European Social Charter guarantees that:

> *'Anyone without adequate resources has the right to social and medical assistance.'*[136]

This imposes an obligation on the Contracting Parties:

> *'to ensure that any person who is without adequate resources and who is unable to secure such resources either by his own efforts or from other sources, in particular by benefits under a social security scheme, be granted adequate assistance, and, in case of sickness, the care necessitated by his condition.'*[137]

The European Committee of Experts has interpreted this provision as making it compulsory to accord assistance to necessitous persons *as of right*. In other words, the States Parties are no longer merely empowered to grant assistance as they think fit; they are under a legal obligation, which they may be called on to honour in court.[138]

4.7.7 Here, too, the wording makes it clear that this right is accorded to *all* those persons – without distinction – who do not have adequate resources of their own. It would therefore not be permissible either to deny social or medical assistance to an individual who meets the economic criteria for it, or to limit the amount of that assistance, solely on the ground that he or she has AIDS. Again, such measures would constitute an interference with the individual's enjoyment of this right, which would have to satisfy the test of necessity. Perhaps the only circumstances in which such 'necessity' could be established would be in a country so poor that every attempt to provide medical care to an AIDS patient, already effectively condemned to death, would demonstrably deprive someone else of a worth-while prolongation of life – in effect, a form of civil 'triage'. But the criterion in such a case must not be AIDS: the same course would have to be followed with everyone else who had a comparable prognosis.

4.7.8 As for the third element of the right to social security, the European Social Charter stipulates that:

'*Everyone has the right to benefit from social welfare services.*'[139]

In order to ensure the effective exercise of this right, the Contracting Parties undertake:

'*to promote or provide services which, by using methods of social work, would contribute to the welfare and development of both individuals and groups in the community, and to their adjustment to the social environment.*'[140]

The European Committee of Experts has interpreted this to mean that a State must promote the establishment of services providing advice and individual help, rather than merely encourage the granting of material assistance.[141]

4.7.9 In this connection, the question arises whether it would be permissible for social workers to withhold their services from an AIDS sufferer and his or her family on the ground that, in providing those services, they run the risk of becoming infected. In seeking the answer, one must bear in mind that one of the tasks of social workers in the face of the challenge posed by AIDS must be to assist those suffering from the disease and their families to cope with it, to adjust to their new situation, and to make the necessary modifications to their lifestyles. Failure to provide that assistance would therefore constitute an interference with the human rights of the sufferer and his or her family to benefit from social welfare services.

4.7.10 As to whether such a withholding of services could be justified on the ground of being necessary to protect the health of the social workers, we have already dealt with this in Section 4.5. above in connection with the right to work. The answer is that it could not: social work entails no contact with blood, semen, or vaginal secretions, and public health experts have made it clear that:

'*In the vast majority of occupations and occupational settings, work does not involve a risk of acquiring or transmitting HIV between workers, from worker to client, or from client to worker.*'[142]

4.8 Freedom from inhuman or degrading treatment or punishment

4.8.1 The global and regional international human rights instruments all provide, in virtually identical terms, that:

> *'No one shall be subjected to torture or to cruel, inhuman or degrading treatment or punishment.'*[143]

In each case, the State's obligation is absolute, and there are no qualifying clauses of any kind. As a result, *any* failure by a State to comply with its obligations in respect of *any* one of these modes of conduct amounts to a violation of this prohibition: no question of justification can ever arise.

4.8.2 In Section 4.2. above, the question was raised as to whether the compulsory segregation or isolation of prisoners with AIDS or HIV infection might amount to a breach of this prohibition. Clearly, such a measure would not constitute 'torture', which the European Court of Human Rights has defined as 'deliberate inhuman treatment causing very serious and cruel suffering'.[144] Might it, though, amount to inhuman or degrading treatment?

4.8.3 According to the European Commission of Human Rights, the notion of 'inhuman' treatment covers at least such treatment as deliberately causes severe suffering, mental or physical, which in the particular situation is unjustifiable.[145] (In a subsequent case, the Commission made it clear that by its use of the term 'unjustifiable' it did not have in mind the possibility that there could ever be a justification for the infliction of inhuman treatment.[146]) The European Court, in the same case, stressed that treatment must attain a minimum level of severity if it is to fall within the scope of the term 'inhuman'. The assessment of this minimum is, in the nature of things, relative; it depends on all the circumstances of the case, such as the duration of the treatment, its physical or mental effects and, in some cases, the sex, age and state of health of the victim.[147]

4.8.4 A few examples may serve to illustrate how this has been applied in practice. The European Commission has expressed the view that solitary confinement of a person under interrogation or awaiting trial, having regard to its strictness, its duration and the end pursued, may constitute inhuman treatment.[148] On the other hand, segregation of a convicted prisoner in order to prevent risk of escape, attack or disturbance of the prison community and to protect him from fellow prisoners has been found not to give rise to any such issue.[149]

4.8.5 'Degrading' treatment is quite a different concept. It has been developed by the European Commission and Court of Human Rights largely, but not exclusively, in the context of interrogation practices. In an early case, the European Commission defined 'degrading treatment' as treatment which 'grossly humiliates [an individual] before others or drives him to act against his will or his conscience'.[150] The European Court of Human Rights applied a similar test when it held that certain techniques used by the British security forces in the interrogation of suspects in Northern Ireland were degrading, 'since they were such as to arouse in their victims feelings of fear, anguish and inferiority capable of humiliating and debasing them and possibly breaking their physical or moral resistance'.[151]

4.8.6 The Commission has made it clear, however, that the expression 'degrading treatment' does not refer to physical acts only. It did so in a case in which it found that British immigration laws discriminated against certain sections of British citizens on the grounds of their colour or race; the Commission concluded that such racial discrimination amounted to degrading treatment.[152] In so finding, the Commission stated that the general purpose of the prohibition of degrading treatment was to prevent interferences with the dignity of human beings of a particularly serious nature. Accordingly, any act which lowers a person in rank, position, reputation, or character can be regarded as degrading treatment if it reaches a certain level of severity, and 'publicly to single out a group of persons for differential treatment on the basis of race might, in certain circumstances, constitute a special form of affront'.

4.8.7 What is clear from these cases is that, for treatment to violate the prohibition against inhuman or degrading treatment, it must reach a certain level of severity. While the compulsory segregation or isolation of prisoners with AIDS or HIV infection would probably not, on that test, constitute 'inhuman' treatment, it might well, depending on the circumstances, amount to 'degrading' treatment –

especially bearing in mind that public health experts have said they see no need for it.[153]

4.8.8 The same might well be the case for various other degrading measures which have not been considered at all in this paper, in the belief that they are unlikely to be contemplated by any sensible modern government.

4.9 The right to equal protection of the law

4.9.1 The principle of non-discrimination is fundamental to the concept of human rights. The primary characteristic which distinguishes 'human' rights from other rights is their universality: according to the classical theory, they are said to 'inhere' in every human being by virtue of his or her humanity alone. It follows that no particular feature or characteristic attaching to any given individual, and which distinguishes that individual from others, can affect his or her entitlement to any *human* rights, whether in degree or in kind, except where the instruments specifically provide for this for a clear and cogent reason – for example, in restricting the right to vote to adults, or in requiring special protection for children.

4.9.2 All the international human rights instruments therefore include a provision which prohibits any form of discrimination in respect of the rights which *they themselves* guarantee. However, that is not the end of the matter, for Article 26 of the International Covenant on Civil and Political Rights reads as follows:

> *'All persons are equal before the law and are entitled without any discrimination to the equal protection of the law. In this respect, the law shall prohibit any discrimination and guarantee to all persons equal and effective protection against discrimination on any ground such as race, colour, sex, language, religion, political or other opinion, national or social origin, property, birth or other status.'*

4.9.3 In two recent cases,[154] the Human Rights Committee (which is the supervisory organ for this Covenant) has had occasion to interpret and apply this provision.

Both of them concerned Dutch unemployment legislation. In each case, the applicants were married women, and the legislation required them to prove that they were 'breadwinners' in order to receive benefits – a condition that did not apply to married men.

4.9.4 In fact, there is nothing in this Covenant from which one might be able to deduce a right to unemployment benefit; the nearest human right is the right to social security which is protected not by this Covenant, but by the other Covenant on Economic, Social and Cultural Rights.[155] However, the Committee said that this Article

> '... *derives from the principle of equal protection of the law without discrimination, as contained in Article 7 of the Universal Declaration of Human Rights, which prohibits discrimination in law or in practice* **in any field regulated and protected by public authorities**. *Article 26 is thus concerned with the obligations imposed on States* **in regard to their legislation and the application thereof**.' (Emphasis added.)

Accordingly, the Committee decided in both these cases that the right to equal protection of the law could be invoked in respect of a right which was *not* guaranteed by the Covenant itself (and one which, moreover, was specifically provided for in another instrument), and concluded that the discrimination on grounds of sex in the Dutch legislation violated this Article of this Covenant.

4.9.5 It follows that the human right to equality before the law, and to the equal protection of the law, extends not only to the 'human' rights guaranteed by the instruments themselves, but may – at all events in some cases – extend to a penumbra of other rights also. So, for example, although there is no human right to eat meals in any particular restaurant, if some country's laws designated some restaurants as being for 'Whites only', and attempted to preclude Blacks from eating there, such a law would violate the provisions of this Article, and would therefore be a denial of the human right to equality before the law. The same would apply to a law which, while not itself designating restaurants, lent its aid to private restaurateurs who expelled Blacks from their premises but not to those who expelled Whites, since such a law would not offer its equal protection to everyone without discrimination.

4.9.6   Now it is noteworthy that the Article uses the phrase 'any discrimination', and that the list of forbidden grounds for discrimination is prefaced by the words 'such as'. The list is therefore not exhaustive. Accordingly, there could be circumstances in which a law which discriminated against people with AIDS or HIV, or which gave them less protection than it gives to others, could constitute a violation of this Article *even if no other human right of the persons concerned were being denied or abridged as a result.*

4.9.7   The areas to which this principle could be applied will vary from one country to another, and will depend on what matters are there regulated by law. The obvious candidates are such things as access to public housing, the grant of licences for various activities, and so on. But there may well be others.

4.9.8   The question then arises what constitutes 'discrimination' for this purpose. In the context of the general anti-discrimination Articles in the relevant instruments, the European Court of Human Rights and the UN Human Rights Committee have both made it clear that not every difference in treatment is necessarily discriminatory. In the leading case delimiting the scope of the non-discrimination guarantee in the European Convention,[156] the European Court of Human Rights held that the principle of equality of treatment was violated if a distinction had no 'objective and reasonable' justification. The existence of such a justification must, the Court stated, be assessed in relation to the aim and effects of the measure under consideration. A difference of treatment in the exercise of a right laid down in the Convention must not only pursue a legitimate aim; there must also be a reasonable relationship of proportionality between the means employed and the aim sought to be realised.[157] In the two cases concerning The Netherlands mentioned above, the Human Rights Committee adopted the same test, stating that the right to non-discrimination demands that any difference in treatment must be based on 'reasonable and objective' criteria.[158]

4.9.9   It follows that an individual with AIDS or HIV may only be subjected to differential treatment, in any field regulated and protected by law by public authorities, if it can be established that the distinction has a legitimate aim (i.e. an objective and reasonable justification) and that the means employed are proportionate to that aim.

4.9.10 Here again, the only imaginable legitimate aim would be the protection of public health. However, public health experts throughout the world are on record as saying that this aim is best pursued by *not* discriminating against those who are infected with HIV, or who suffer from AIDS. To take just three examples:

> *'Discrimination against, and stigmatization of, HIV-infected people and people with AIDS and population groups undermine public health and must be avoided.'*[159]

> *'The avoidance of discrimination against persons known or suspected to be HIV-infected is important for AIDS prevention and control: failure to prevent such discrimination may endanger public health.'*[160]

> *'... discrimination may endanger public health; stigmatization may itself represent a threat to public health. ... protecting the human rights and dignity of HIV-infected people, including people with AIDS, and members of population groups, is not a luxury – it is a necessity. It is not a question of the 'rights of the many' against the 'rights of the few'; the protection of the uninfected majority depends upon and is inextricably bound with the protection of the rights and dignity of the infected persons.'*[161]

In that situation, it is difficult to see how discrimination against AIDS sufferers or HIV carriers in respect of *any* of their legal rights, or their protection by the law, in any field regulated by public authorities could be justified as a measure that is proportionate to the legitimate aim of seeking to limit the spread of this infection.

4.10 Public emergencies

4.10.1 Like other epidemics, AIDS is often loosely referred to – especially in the sensational press – as presenting 'a public emergency'. We therefore need to consider the provisions which international human rights law contains on this subject.

4.10.2 Each of the main international human rights instruments[162] allows its State Parties to 'derogate from' some of the rights which it guarantees in the event of a 'public emergency which threatens the life of the nation'.[163] So, for example, the International Covenant on Civil and Political Rights provides that:

> *'In time of public emergency which threatens the life of the nation and the existence of which is officially proclaimed, the State Parties to the present Covenant may take measures derogating from their obligations under the present Covenant to the extent strictly required by the exigencies of the situation, provided that such measures are not inconsistent with their other obligations under international law ...'[164]*

However, another paragraph of the same Article always excepts from this provision a number of the rights guaranteed by the instrument: in particular, the right to life, the freedom from cruel, inhuman or degrading treatment or punishment, and the freedom from slavery. Even in the course of the most extreme public emergency, therefore, there may not be *any* derogation from *any* of these rights and freedoms.

4.10.3 Derogating from the obligation to respect a human right is far more drastic than limiting or restricting it within the margins permitted by the instrument, for it allows – albeit only 'to the extent strictly required by the exigencies of the situation' – the complete suspension of the right concerned. It is the kind of measure normally only undertaken in times of war, or at a level of civil disorder which leads to a declaration of martial law – such as suspending the right to freedom of movement by a curfew, or the right to liberty by arrest and internment without trial. The Human Rights Committee, and the European Commission and Court of Human Rights, have all emphasised that derogation is a quite exceptional measure, both the imposition and the extent of which needs to be strictly justified by the State concerned.

4.10.4 In an early case,[165] the European Court of Human Rights held that the natural and customary meaning of the words 'a public emergency threatening the life of the nation' was sufficiently clear: they referred to an exceptional situation of crisis or emergency which affected the whole population and constituted a threat to the organised life of the community of which the State was composed. The European Commission of Human Rights subsequently elaborated on this, distinguishing four separate elements in this definition, namely that:

- the public emergency must be actual and imminent;

- its effects must involve the whole nation;

- the continuance of the organised life of the nation must be threatened; and

- the crisis or danger must be exceptional, in that the normal measures or restrictions permitted by the Convention for the maintenance of public safety, health, and order are plainly inadequate.[166]

4.10.5   Both the Commission and the Court have said that although some discretion and 'margin of appreciation' must be allowed to a government in determining whether there exists a public emergency threatening the life of the nation which must be dealt with by exceptional measures derogating from its normal obligations under the Convention, the supervisory organs have the competence and the duty to examine and pronounce upon a government's determination of the existence of such an emergency. As the Court put it in a later case, 'the domestic margin of appreciation is [thus] accompanied by a European supervision'.[167]

4.10.6   That this supervision is very real is demonstrated by the findings of the Commission and the Court in cases in which the respondent government has sought to justify measures derogating from its obligations under the Convention by invoking a public emergency. In two cases involving special powers of arrest and detention without trial of persons suspected of terrorist activities, respectively introduced in Ireland and in Northern Ireland in 1957 and 1971-75, the European Court found these measures, although in breach of the governments' obligations under the guarantee of the right to liberty, to be justified measures of derogation.[168] The existence of a 'public emergency threatening the life of the nation' had, the Court found, been reasonably deduced by the respective governments from a combination of several factors, including the activities of a secret army (the IRA) engaged in unconstitutional activities and using violence to attain its purposes, and the increase in the level of terrorist activities. Moreover, these measures were no more than was 'strictly required by the exigencies of the situation'.

4.10.7 By contrast, in the *Greek case*,[169] the respondent 'government of the colonels' contended that, when they had seized power in Greece by military force on 21 April 1967 and had overthrown the legitimate government, there was a public emergency threatening the life of the nation, composed of three factors: the threat of a Communist take-over of the government by force; the state of public order; and the constitutional crisis immediately preceding the general election due to be held in May 1967. The Commission fully investigated the government's assertions, and came to the conclusion that none of these factors was present at that time in any measure sufficient to constitute a 'public emergency threatening the life of the nation'. In the result, the respondent government stood convicted of gross and wholly unjustified violations of the Convention, left the Council of Europe in order to avoid being expelled from it, and was overthrown by its internal opponents not many years later.

4.10.8 It follows that it is not open to a State simply to declare a public emergency in order to seek to justify measures that would otherwise be a breach of its international obligations. Whether such an emergency exists is, ultimately, a matter for objective assessment by the international supervisory organs in the human rights field, as is the question whether the measures taken by the State did or did not exceed those 'strictly required by the exigencies of the situation'.

4.10.9 The question then arises whether the prevalence of AIDS within a country could ever be so high as to amount to 'a public emergency threatening the life of the nation', and so entitle the government of that country to introduce drastic measures to suspend the human rights of its inhabitants. It is difficult to imagine such a situation in the case of a disease which does not have the dramatic virulence of, say, a mediaeval outburst of bubonic plague: the effects of the disease would have to involve the entire nation, and threaten the continuance of its whole organised life.

4.10.10 However, even if one could imagine a scenario where AIDS threatened the survival of an entire nation, one can only speculate what considerations would then need to be weighed in the balance. Much would of course depend on whether, by then, any efficient vaccine or cure had been found. If it had, there would certainly be powerful arguments for administering it, if necessary by compulsion –

perhaps even if this entailed some incidental risk to the health of a few. However, in the absence of such a vaccine or cure, it is difficult to see how even the most drastic measures could help to prevent the further spread of a disease with such limited infectivity and such a long incubation period, and so justify derogations on the ground of a public emergency.

5 Conclusions

5.0 In this final Section, we shall attempt to summarise the conclusions we have reached, with references to the earlier Sections in which the supporting arguments for them may be found.

5.1 Generally

5.1.1 The following public health measures, designed to counter the spread of HIV infection, entail no adverse consequences for the human rights of any individuals, and are therefore unobjectionable on human rights grounds (Section 3.3.1.):

- research into the pathophysiology of the disease, its modes of transmission, and the development of vaccines and curative drugs;

- ensuring the safety of blood for transfusions, blood products for use in treatment, semen for artificial insemination, and other cells, tissues and organs for transplantation;

- preventing the re-use of needles, syringes and other skin-piercing or invasive equipment without proper sterilisation;

- making safety measures, such as condoms and sterile syringes, more widely available, especially to high-risk groups;

- health information, education and promotion programmes, directed either at the general public or to groups particularly at risk – such as prostitutes of either sex, their customers, drug abusers, and – in the developed countries – homosexual and bisexual men.

5.1.2 The following measures may have adverse consequences, but would be acceptable on human rights grounds provided that they are undertaken completely voluntarily – that is, only after a full explanation of all the possible consequences, and with the explicit, free and informed consent of the persons concerned, obtained without the application of any illicit pressures, whether in the form of promises or of threats (Section 3.3.2.):

- the voluntary testing of individuals for HIV seropositivity, either on an 'anonymous' basis (that is, without being required to give a true name, or any other identifying particulars), or with stringent safeguards for confidentiality;

- the counselling of individuals, both before and after they are tested;

- their voluntary treatment to mitigate the effects of infection, or to achieve modifications of their behaviour which they themselves desire.

5.1.3 The following measures would, in present circumstances, constitute interferences with the human right to privacy of the individuals concerned, and would not be justifiable under international human rights law on public health (or any other) grounds:

- the *mandatory* testing of any individuals (other than voluntary donors of blood, semen, or other tissues or organs) for HIV-seropositivity, however they are selected (Section 4.1.1.);

- the compulsory registration of suspected HIV carriers (Section 4.1.2.)

- the mandatory collection, storage and processing by a public authority of *identifiable* personal information about AIDS sufferers or HIV carriers – for instance, by making either or both of these a 'notifiable disease' by law – *without* protecting the information concerned by the strictest rules of medical confidentiality or, better still, by anonymity (Sections 4.1.3. and 4.1.4.);

- the disclosure of the results of HIV tests to third persons (including health professionals) without the patients' consent, or permitting the improper discovery of such results by third persons (Section 4.1.5.).

5.1.4   On the other hand, the following measures, while entailing some interference with the human right to privacy, might be justified on public health grounds:

- in exceptional circumstances, informing someone at risk of a patient's known HIV-positive status, even in breach of medical confidence – e.g. where the patient refuses, despite counselling and advice, to take the necessary precautions not to pass on the infection to a known sexual partner, or if the patient is a health worker and is consistently negligent in observing routine hygiene precautions, or fails to follow medical advice about his or her work – provided the circumstances in which this was allowed are clearly defined by law (Section 4.1.5.);

- making it a criminal offence for an HIV carrier knowingly or recklessly to infect others, provided that the offence could be defined sufficiently precisely to meet the requirements of legal certainty and foreseeability. However, to criminalise (or recriminalise) male homosexual conduct could not be justified on any ground in human rights law. (Section 4.1.6.).

5.1.5   The following measures would not constitute interferences with the human right to privacy of the individuals concerned:

- estimating the prevalence of HIV infection in existing populations, by testing fractions of samples which have been taken from patients, with their consent, for other purposes, and have then been so completely anonymised as to make it impossible to relate them back to the individuals from whom they were taken (Section 4.1.3.);

- making AIDS or HIV infection a 'notifiable disease', if the information reported was either wholly anonymous in the first place, or was protected by the strictest compliance with the general rules of medical confidentiality – that is, that it could only be released either anonymously, or with the explicit and informed consent of the person to whom it relates (Section 4.1.4.);

5.1.6 The following measures would entail violations of the human right to liberty and security, and could not be justified on public health (or any other) grounds (Section 4.2.):

- compulsory blood tests;

- compulsory quarantine, e.g. by enforced admission to a hospital or a hospice;

- compulsory internment in a colony removed from the rest of society (along the lines of a leper colony).

5.1.7 The following measures, although they entail a violation of the human right to liberty and security, might be justifiable on grounds of public health, provided that the person detained has the right to have the lawfulness of his or her detention tested initially, and thereafter periodically, by an independent judicial tribunal (Section 4.2.):

- the detention in an emergency of an individual known, or suspected on cogent grounds, to be HIV-positive while he or she presents an acute risk of infection to others and is unable to take care of him or herself;

- the detention of an individual while he or she is deliberately trying to infect others with HIV.

5.1.8 As for the human right to freedom of movement, it would not be legitimate for a State:

- to make the entry into the country of its own returning nationals conditional on their taking an HIV test, let alone on obtaining a negative result;

- to restrict, on AIDS/HIV grounds, the entry of aliens whom it is bound to admit by some specific treaty, as in the case of the European Community or the European Convention on Establishment;

- to restrict, on such grounds, the entry of aliens where this would interfere with their enjoyment of other rights guaranteed to them under international human rights law, such as the right to family life;

- to restrict on such grounds, either for nationals or for aliens lawfully within its territory, liberty of movement within that territory or the freedom to choose a residence.

5.1.9 The following would also be violations of the human right to freedom of movement, if it were done on the grounds of AIDS or HIV-positivity:

- the *arbitrary* expulsion of a citizen by any State Party to the International Covenant on Civil and Political Rights or the African Charter;

- *any* expulsion of a citizen by any State Party to either the European or the American Convention on Human Rights;

- the *collective* expulsion of aliens by a State Party to any of the three regional treaties;

- the *individual* expulsion of any alien by any State Party to the Covenant, the American Convention or the African Charter otherwise than 'in accordance with the law' and, in the case of a State Party to the Covenant, if he or she has not had the opportunity to submit reasons against the expulsion to a competent authority. (Section 4.3.)

5.1.10 The human right to equality before the law, and to the equal protection of the law, would render it illegitimate to discriminate against individuals on the grounds of AIDS or HIV-positivity not only in respect of their human rights specifically protected by the code, but also in any other fields legally regulated by public authorities, such as access to public housing, licences, etc. (Section 4.9.)

5.1.11 To justify the *suspension* – and not merely the various restrictions and limitations discussed in this paper – of any of the human rights and fundamental freedoms guaranteed by international law, there would have to be a 'public emergency threatening the life of the nation' on such a scale as to involve the entire nation, and threaten the continuance of its whole organised life. Even in such a situation, it is difficult to see what suspensions of human rights could be justified in the absence of a vaccine or cure. (Section 4.10.)

5.2 AIDS, marriage, and procreation

5.2.1 A prohibition of marriage for persons known to be HIV-positive would be an interference with the substance of the human right to marry, and could not be justified on any grounds.

5.2.2 Compulsory HIV tests for persons who wish to marry, and the communication of each of their results to the other without their consent, would be an interference with the human right to privacy and could not be justified on any grounds.

5.2.3 On the other hand, the provision of information about AIDS, and the offer of *voluntary* HIV tests, to marriage candidates would not be open to any objection on human rights grounds.

5.2.4 *Mandatory* abortions or sterilisations for HIV-infected women would be a violation of the human right to found a family, and could not be justified on any grounds. (Section 4.4.).

5.3 AIDS and employment

5.3.1 In the context of the right to work protected by international human rights law, an applicant for a job could not be legitimately refused employment, nor could an employee be legitimately dismissed, solely on the ground that he or she was – or was suspected of being – HIV-positive, unless it could be objectively established that the absence of infection was a *bona fide* and *necessary* occupational qualification, or that the infection would clearly and substantially affect job performance.

5.3.2 For example, there might be no interference with the right to work if someone who was HIV-positive were not employed in a position requiring travel to countries which bar those so infected. Nor might there be such an interference if persons were not employed because they were already displaying some symptoms of fully developed AIDS, and their prognosis was such that they would either not be in the position long enough, or not be in sufficiently good health, to be able to carry out the normal duties of the employment. However, in any such case the situation would be no different than if such persons were suffering from any other disease having the same effect on their performance at work.

5.3.3 The currently available evidence of risk of HIV infection leading to neuro-psychiatric disorders would not be a sufficient reason for not employing infected persons in sensitive occupations such as train drivers or commercial pilots. Nor, on present evidence, do there appear to be any tenable grounds for restricting the involvement of those who are HIV-positive in the preparation or distribution of food.

5.3.4 The human right of all workers to 'safe and healthy working conditions' could not be invoked to justify refusing to employ, or dismissing, someone who is HIV-positive (or who refuses to reveal whether he or she is HIV-positive), on the ground that his or her presence constitutes a danger to their fellow workers: such a measure would not meet the test of necessity.

5.3.5 In exceptional circumstances – e.g. if he or she were consistently negligent in observing routine hygiene precautions, or failed to follow medical advice about their work – it might be justified to interfere with the right to work of an HIV-infected *health* worker. (Section 4.5.)

5.3.6 It would not be justified to discriminate in any way against AIDS victims in respect of their rights to public social security, social and medical assistance, or social welfare services. (Section 4.7.)

5.4 AIDS and schools

Apart from some exceptional cases – such as children who, by reason of delayed development of neurological handicap, lack control of their body secretions – the fact of HIV infection should not be a factor taken into account in any matters concerning school admissions, transfers, attendance, or exclusion from school. If it is, that might constitute an unjustifiable restriction on the human right to education. (Section 4.6.)

5.5 AIDS and prisons

The compulsory segregation or isolation of prisoners with AIDS or HIV infection might well, depending on the circumstances, violate the international prohibition of 'degrading treatment'. (Section 4.8.)

6 *Notes*

1 AIDS

1 See *Guidelines for the development of a national AIDS prevention and control programme* (WHO, Geneva, 1988), p. 3.

2 Human Rights

2 For a simple introduction to this code, see Sieghart, P.,*The Lawful Rights of Mankind* (Oxford, 1985), German translation: *Die geltenden Menschenrechte* (Strasbourg, 1988); for the full texts with commentary and a digest of the relevant case-law, see *The International Law of Human Rights* (Oxford, 1983), by the same author.

3 The United Kingdom is bound by both the Covenants, the European Convention, and the European Social Charter.

4 This is the formulation used in Art. 8 of the European Convention on Human Rights.

5 *The Handyside Case*, Judgment of the European Court of Human Rights (1976) 1 EHRR 737, para. 48; *The Sunday Times Case*, Judgment of the European Court of Human Rights (1979) 2 EHRR 245, para. 59.

6 *The Handyside Case* supra, para. 48; *The Sunday Times Case*, supra, para. 59.

7 *The Handyside Case*, supra, para. 49; *The Sunday Times Case*, supra, para. 59.

8 *The Sunday Times Case*, supra, para. 59.

9 *Young, James and Webster v. United Kingdom*, Judgment of the European Court of Human Rights (1981) 4 EHRR 38.

10 *The Handyside Case*, supra, paras. 48-50; *The Sunday Times Case*, supra, para. 62.

11 *The Handyside Case*, supra, para. 48; *The Sunday Times Case*, supra, para. 59.

12 *The Sunday Times Case*, supra, para. 60.

13   *The Sunday Times Case*, supra, para. 63; see also the *Barthold Case*, Judgment of the European Court of Human Rights, (1985) 7 EHRR 383, paras. 79-81.

14   *The Sunday Times Case*, supra, para. 65.

15   *The Sunday Times Case*, supra, para. 66.

16   *The Sunday Times Case*, supra, para. 61.

17   *De Becker v. Belgium*, Report of the European Commission of Human Rights (1962) 1 EHRR 43.

18   Porter, R., Plague and panic, *New Society*, 12 December 1986.

3   AIDS and Human Rights

19   See Curson, P.H., *Times of Crisis* (Sydney, 1985).

20   *Guidelines for the development of a national AIDS prevention and control programme* (WHO, Geneva, 1988), p. 21.

21   For bubonic plague, it is generally less than 6 days, and 50% of those who develop it die within 8 days. For diphtheria, it is around 2 to 4 days. For gonorrhoea - the most common sexually transmitted disease - it is around 2 to 7 days for men, and sometimes a little longer for women.

22   For a powerful evocation of the horrors of the disease, see Henrik Ibsen's play *Ghosts*.

23   In 1913, it was estimated that anything up to 500,000 people were infected with it in London alone: see Porter, R. and Porter D., *AIDS: Law, Liberty and Public Health* in Byrne, P. (ed.), *Health, Rights and Resources* (London, 1988), p. 89 and references there cited.

24   *Ibid.*, pp. 90-92.

25   *Global Programme on AIDS: Progress Report No. 4* (WHO, Geneva, 1988), p. 7.

26   *Ibid.* See also *Social aspects of AIDS Prevention and Control Programmes* (WHO, Geneva, 1987).

27   See, for example, *AIDS diagnosis and control: current situation* (WHO, Geneva, 1987); *Screening and testing in AIDS prevention and control programmes* (WHO, Geneva, 1988); *Counselling in HIV infection and disease* (WHO, Geneva, 1988).

28   See Kirby, M.D, AIDS legislation - turning up the heat?, *Journal of Medical Ethics* (1986) **12**, 187.

29   According to WHO, 'Routine screening of the whole population for HIV antibody is unnecessary and unrealistic': *AIDS diagnosis and control: current situation* (WHO, Geneva, 1987).

30   *The Independent*, 21 June 1988, p. 11. (The report went on to point out that the Prime Minister of the country concerned was married to a foreigner.)

31   See above, note 29.

32   *The Sunday Times Case*, supra.

33 It is principally against deprivation of life falling within these categories that the relevant provisions in the treaties are directed. In addition, they all contain exceptions, e.g. for the lawful imposition of the death penalty for exceptionally serious crimes, or in defence of the person from unlawful violence, etc.

34 *X v. Ireland* (6040/73), Decision of the European Commission of Human Rights, CD 44, 121.

35 *Association X v. United Kingdom* (7154/75), Decision of the European Commission of Human Rights, DR 14, 31.

4   The relevant rights and freedoms

36 *Belgian Linguistic Case*, Judgment (1968) 1 EHRR 252.

37 *Dudgeon v. United Kingdom*, Judgment of the European Court of Human Rights (1981) 4 EHRR 149.

38 *X v. Austria* (8278/78), Decision (1979) DR 18, 154. The Commission found that this test also constituted a deprivation of liberty: see Section 4.2 below.

39 (10435/83), Decision (1984) DR 40, 251.

40 As in the case of smallpox, where widespread vaccination campaigns eventually led to the world-wide eradication of the disease.

41 See *Social aspects of AIDS Prevention and Control Programmes* (WHO, Geneva, 1987); *Screening and testing in AIDS prevention and control programmes* (WHO, Geneva, 1988).

42 See *AIDS diagnosis and control: current situation* (WHO, Geneva, 1987), p. 11; *AIDS: Discrimination and Public Health*, Address to the IV International Conference on AIDS, Stockholm, 13 June 1988, by Dr. Jonathan Mann, Director, Global Programme on Aids, WHO. This appears in fact to have begun to happen in Bavaria: see Behr, U. and Görgens, K., *Auswirkungen des Bayrischen Massnahmenkataloges auf die Beratungs - und Behandlungsarbeit Bayrischer Einrichtungen* (Deutsche Aids-Hilfe, Berlin, 1988); Exiles, *Man Alive!*, 8 January 1988.

43 *AIDS diagnosis and control: current situation* (WHO, Geneva, 1987), p. 3.

44 *AIDS: Discrimination and Public Health*, address to the IV International Conference on AIDS, Stockholm, 13 June 1988.

45 *London Declaration on AIDS Prevention*, 28 January 1988, para. 4.

46 See, e.g., *SIECUS Report* (1987) **16**, 1 at p. 4, and references there cited; Fife, K.H. et al., *Behavioral changes among sexually active homosexual men after learning they are negative for HIV antibody* (Indiana University School of Medicine, Indianapolis).

47 *Guidelines for the Drawing up of a Public Health Policy to Fight Aids*, Appendix to Recommendation No. R (87) 25 Concerning a Common European Public Health Policy to Fight the Acquired Immunodeficiency Syndrome (AIDS), adopted by the Committee of Ministers on 26 November 1987, para. 2.2.1.

48 See *Leander v. Sweden*, Judgment of the European Court of Human Rights (1987) 9 EHRR 433.

49 See, for example, Fehrs, L.J. et al., *Anonymous vs Confidential HIV Testing: Results of a Trial in Oregon* (Centers for Disease Control, Oregon State Health Division).

50   For example, to be reasonably certain that an apparent doubling of prevalence from 1 per 1000 to 2 per 1000 was not a chance effect would require samples from 12,000 truly random subjects on each of two occasions: *Report of a Working Group on the Monitoring and Surveillance of HIV Infection and AIDS* (Department of Health and Social Security, London, 1988), para. 3.8.

51   This will soon be undertaken in the United Kingdom: see Department of Health Press Release, 23 November 1988.

52   See, for an example of the general acceptance of this proposition within the Member States of the Council of Europe, Article 6 of the Convention for the Protection of Individuals with Regard to Automatic Processing of Personal Information:

'... personal data concerning health or sexual life may not be processed automatically unless domestic law provides appropriate safeguards.'

Various national laws of the Member States now also reflect this provision.

53   See, e.g., Gen Ohi et al., *Change in Acceptance rate for HIV testing when AIDS is notifiable* (Teikyo University School of Medicine, Tokyo); Meacham, S. et al., *AIDS screening: who is willing to be tested?* (UC Berkeley/UC San Francisco Joint Medical Program); Sy, F.S. et al., *The impact of mandatory reporting of HIV seropositive persons in South Carolina* (University of South Carolina School of Public Health, Columbia).

54   Appendix to Recommendation No. R (87) 25, para. 2.2.4.

55   The disclosure to, or improper discovery by, third persons of facts relating to an individual's physical condition, health or personality has been found by the European Commission of Human Rights to constitute an interference with his private life: *Van Oosterwijck v. Belgium*, Report (1979) 3 EHRR 581. See also *X v. Norway*, Decision (1978) DR 14, 228.

56   From Surgeon General C. Everett Koop's *Report on AIDS* (as cited in *SIECUS Report* (1987) **16**, 1 at p. 8).

57   For details of these cases, see *AIDS: HIV-infected Health Care Workers* (UK Health Departments, HMSO, London, 1988), Appendix 2.

58   *AIDS diagnosis and control: current situation* (WHO, Geneva, 1987), p. 3; see also the French official circular DH/DGS of 28 October 1987: 'systematic screening of all hospital patients is inappropriate and entails costs that are wholly disproportionate to the results to be anticipated'.

59   Appendix to Recommendation No. R (87) 25, para. 2.2.3.

60   See *Duties of Doctors Infected with HIV or Suffering from AIDS*, Statement by the President of the General Medical Council (London, 1987).

61   *The Sunday Times Case*, Judgment of the European Court of Human Rights (1979) 2 EHRR 245.

62   Judgment (1981) 4 EHRR 149.

63   Judgment (1988), to be reported as Series A, Volume 142.

64   *Engel v. The Netherlands* (No. 1), Judgment (1976) 1 EHRR 647 at 669.

65   *Ibid.*

66   Universal Declaration of Human Rights, Art. 9; International Covenant on Civil and Political Rights, Art. 9(1); American Convention on Human Rights, Art. 7(3); African Charter on Human Rights and Peoples' Rights, Art. 6.

67   *Engel v. The Netherlands* (No. 1), supra, at 670; *Guzzardi v Italy*, Judgment of the European Court of Human Rights (1980) 3 EHRR 333 at 362-63.

68   *X v. Austria* (8278/78), Decision of the Commission (1979) DR 18, 154.

69   *Guzzardi v. Italy*, supra, at 363-4.

70   *X v. Switzerland* (7754/77), Decision of the Commission (1977) DR 11, 216.

71   Article 5(1)(e).

72   *Lawless v. Ireland*, Judgment of the Court (1961) 1 EHRR 15, at paras. 14-15; *Caprino v. United Kingdom* (6871/75), Report of the Commission (1980) DR 12, 14 at 20; *Bouamar v. Belgium* Judgment of the Court (1988) not yet reported.

73   *Caprino v. United Kingdom*, supra, at 19-20.

74   *Winterwerp v. The Netherlands*, Judgment of the Court (1979) 2 EHRR 387. However, in *X v. United Kingdom*, Judgment (1981) 4 EHRR 188, the Court explained (at para. 41) that the 'objective medical expertise' need not in all conceivable cases be obtained before, rather than after, the confinement of the person concerned: where an emergency required the immediate confinement of a person capable of presenting a danger to others, it would be impracticable to require a thorough medical examination before arrest or detention.

75   *Social aspects of AIDS Prevention and Control Programmes* (WHO, Geneva, 1987).

76   *Ibid.*

77   Appendix to Recommendation No. R (87) 25, para. 2.2.2.

78   *Statement from the Consultation on Prevention and Control of AIDS in Prisons* (WHO, Geneva, 1987), para. C.4.

79   International Covenant on Civil and Political Rights, Art. 9(4); European Convention on Human Rights, Art. 5(4); American Convention on Human Rights, Art. 7(6).

80   *Winterwerp v. The Netherlands*, Judgment of the Court (1979) 2 EHRR 387; *X v. United Kingdom*, Judgment of the Court (1981) 4 EHRR 188.

81   *Van Droogenbroek v. Belgium*, Judgment of the Court (1982) 4 EHRR 443; *Weeks v. United Kingdom*, Judgment of the Court (1987) 10 EHRR 293.

82   Art. 3(2) of Protocol No. 4; see also Art. 12(4) of the International Covenant on Civil and Political Rights, and Art. 22(5) of the American Convention on Human Rights. Note, however, that several States, including the UK, have not ratified Protocol No. 4, and/or have entered reservations to Art. 12 of the Covenant.

83   See Goodwin-Gill, G. *International Law and the Movement of Persons between States* (Oxford, 1978) at p. 196.

84   European Treaty Series No. 19.

85   *Statement on screening of international travellers for infection with HIV* (WHO, Geneva, 1987).

86   Appendix to Recommendation No. R (87) 25, para. 2.2.2.

87   Art. 12(1); see also Universal Declaration, Art. 13(1), European Convention, Protocol No. 4, Art. 2(1); American Convention, Art. 22(1); African Charter, Art. 12(1).

88   *Cyprus v. Turkey*, Report of the Commission, 10 July 1976.

89   Appendix to Resolution No. R (87) 25, para. 2.2.2.

90   DGS/1 C No. 784 of 8 December 1987.

91   Protocol No. 4, Art. 3(1).

92   Art. 12(4)

93   Art. 13.

94   *F v. Switzerland*, Judgment of the Court (1987) 10 EHRR 411; *Rees v. United Kingdom*, Judgment of the Court (1986) 9 EHRR 56; *Hamer v. United Kingdom*, Report of the Commission (1979) DR 24, 5; *Draper v. United Kingdom*, Report of the Commission (1980) DR 24, 72.

95   *Draper v. United Kingdom*, supra, at 79; *Rees v. United Kingdom*, supra; *F v. Switzerland*, supra.

96   *Rees v. United Kingdom*, supra, para. 50; *F v. Switzerland*, supra, para. 32.

97   *F v. Switzerland*, supra.

98   *Hamer and Draper v. United Kingdom*, supra (prohibitions on prisoners marrying while in custody); *F v. Switzerland*, supra (temporary prohibition of remarriage).

99   See, for example, *Marckx v. Belgium*, Judgment of the European Court of Human Rights (1979) 2 EHRR 330.

100   See, for example, *SIECUS Report* **16**, 1, p. 5, and references there cited.

101   *AIDS diagnosis and control: current situation* (WHO, Geneva, 1987), p. 3.

102   Cf., mutatis mutandis, *F v. Switzerland*, supra.

103   In June 1987, the WHO was estimating it at between 25% and 50%: *Statement from the Consultation on Breast-feeding/Breast Milk and Human Immunodeficiency Virus (HIV)* (WHO, Geneva, 1987).

104   In an unpublished Decision (1287/61), referred to in Jacobs, F.G., *The European Convention on Human Rights* (Oxford, 1975), the European Commission has said that this might involve an infringement of the right to life.

105   Universal Declaration of Human Rights, Art. 23(1); International Covenant on Economic, Social and Cultural Rights, Art. 6(1); African Charter, Art. 15.

106   Including the European Social Charter, Art. 1.

107 See, for example, the Committee's consideration of the Report submitted by The Netherlands: 'Without a fundamental guarantee against arbitrary dismissal, the right to work would be meaningless'. (*Summary Record of the Committee on Economic, Social and Cultural Rights*, E/C.12/1987/SR.5 at p. 3.)

108 Conclusions I, 15.

109 Conclusions I, 166.

110 *Statement from the Consultation on AIDS and the Workplace* (WHO, in association with ILO, Geneva, 1988).

111 *The Employment Implications of AIDS* (Engineering Employers' Federation, London, 1987).

112 *Ibid.*

113 *Statement on Neuropsychological Aspects of HIV infection* (WHO, Geneva, 1988).

114 *Social Aspects of AIDS Prevention and Control Programmes* (WHO, Geneva, 1987).

115 European Social Charter, Art. 31(1). The Covenant, by contrast, permits only such limitations as are 'determined by law only in so far as this may be compatible with the nature of these rights and solely for the purpose of promoting the general welfare in a democratic society' (Art.4).

116 This right is guaranteed by Art. 7 of the International Covenant on Economic, Social and Cultural Rights, and Art. 3 of the European Social Charter.

117 *Social Aspects of AIDS Prevention and Control Programmes* (WHO, Geneva, 1987).

118 *Statement from the Consultation on AIDS and the Workplace* (WHO, in association with ILO, Geneva, 1988).

119 *Ibid.*

120 Appendix to Recommendation No. R (87) 25, para. 2.2.2.

121 *AIDS: HIV-infected Health Care Workers* (UK Health Departments, HMSO, London, 1988), paras. 6 and 13.

122 Art. 13.

123 Art. 2 of Protocol No. 1.

124 *Belgian Linguistic Case*, Judgment (1968) 1 EHRR 252.

125 *Ibid.*

126 *Campbell and Cosans v. United Kingdom*, Judgment (1982) 4 EHRR 293.

127 *Social Aspects of AIDS Prevention and Control Programme* (WHO, Geneva, 1987).

128 Appendix to Recommendation No. R (87) 25, para. 2.2.2.

129 See, for example, *Children at School and Problems relating to AIDS* (Department of Education and Science and Welsh Office, London, 1986).

130   Art. 9.

131   Part I, Art. 12.

132   Part II, Art. 12, para. 1.

133   Part II, Art. 12, para. 2.

134   Conclusions IV, 81.

135   European Social Charter, Art. 31(1). The equivalent provision of the International Covenant on Economic, Social and Cultural Rights is even stricter:

'... the State may subject such rights only to such limitations as are determined by law only in so far as this may be compatible with the nature of these rights and solely for the purpose of promoting the general welfare in a democratic society.' (Art. 4).

136   Part I, Art. 13.

137   Part II, Art. 13, para. 1.

138   Conclusions I, 64.

139   Part I, Art. 14.

140   Part II, Art. 14, para. 1.

141   Conclusions I, 69.

142   *Statement from the Consultation on AIDS and the Workplace* (WHO, Geneva, 1988).

143   Art. 5 of the Universal Declaration, Art. 7 of the International Covenant on Civil and Political Rights, Article 5(2) of the American Convention on Human Rights, and Art. 5 of the African Charter. Art. 3 of the European Convention leaves out the word 'cruel'.

144   *Ireland v. United Kingdom*, Judgment (1978) 2 EHRR 25 at 80.

145   *Denmark et al. v. Greece*, Report (1969) YB 12 bis.

146   *Ireland v. the United Kingdom*, Report (1976).

147   *Ireland v. United Kingdom*, Judgment (1978) 2 EHRR 25.

148   *Krause v. Switzerland*, Decision (1977) DR 13, 73.

149   *Ensslin, Baader and Raspe v. Federal Republic of Germany*, Decision (1976) DR 14, 64.

150   *Denmark et al. v. Greece*, Report (1969) YB 12 bis.

151   *Ireland v. United Kingdom*, Judgment (1978) 2 EHRR 25 at 80.

152   *East African Asians Case*, Report (1973) 3 EHRR 76.

153   *Statement from the Consultation on Prevention and Control of AIDS in Prisons* (WHO, Geneva, 1987), para. C.4.

154   *S.W.M. Broeks v. The Netherlands*, Communication No. 172/1984, Views adopted by the Human Rights Committee (1987), *Report of the Human Rights Committee*, UN General Assembly Official Records: Forty-Second Session, Supplement No. 40 (A/42/40), p. 139; and *F.H. Zwaan-de Vries v. The Netherlands*, Communication No. 182/1984, *ibid.*, p. 160.

155   Art. 9.

156   *Belgian Linguistic Case*, Judgment of the European Court of Human Rights (1968) 1 EHRR 252.

157   *Ibid.*, at 284; cf. *De Geillustreerde Pers N.V. v. The Netherlands*, Report of the Commission (1976) DR 8, 5 at 14-15.

158   *S.W.M. Broeks v. the Netherlands*, loc. cit. at p. 150; and *F.H. Zwaan-de Vries v. the Netherlands*, loc. cit. at 168.

159   World Summit of Ministers of Health, *London Declaration on AIDS Prevention*, 28 January 1988.

160   *Social aspects of AIDS Prevention and Control Programmes* (WHO, Geneva, 1987).

161   *AIDS: Discrimination and Public Health*, Address to the IV International Conference on AIDS, Stockholm, 13 June 1988, by Dr. Jonathan Mann, Director, Global Programme on Aids, WHO.

162   Apart from the International Covenant on Economic, Social and Cultural Rights, and the African Charter.

163   In the words of the European Convention on Human Rights, Art. 15, and the International Covenant on Civil and Political Rights, Art. 4(1). The American Convention on Human Rights (Art. 27(1)) speaks instead of 'public danger, or other emergency that threatens the independence or security of a State Party'.

164   Article 4(1).

165   *Lawless v. Ireland*, Judgment (1961) 1 EHRR 15.

166   *Denmark, Norway, Sweden and The Netherlands v. Greece*, Report (1969) YB 12 bis.

167   *Ireland v. United Kingdom*, Judgment (1978) 2 EHRR 25.

168   *Lawless v. Ireland*, Judgment (1961) 1 EHRR 15; *Ireland v.* United Kingdom, Judgment (1978) 2 EHRR 25.

169   *Denmark, Norway, Sweden and The Netherlands v. Greece*, Report of the Commission (1969) YB 12 bis.

Table of Authorities

Index